KU-334-687

Foreword

CIRIA's research programme *Methane and associated hazards to construction* is intended to provide guidance for the construction industry. In addition to a bibliography relevant to methane and construction (CIRIA Special Publication 79) and a study of the construction industry's needs for research and information on methane (CIRIA Project Report 5), the publications of the programme include guidance documents on the nature, occurrence and hazards of methane (CIRIA Report 130), on detection, measurement and monitoring (CIRIA Report 131) and on protecting development from methane (CIRIA Report 149). Current CIRIA research projects deal with the interpretation of subsurface gas concentrations and with the assessment of risk.

This report dealing with the strategies of investigation is the result of the sixth project in the programme. It was prepared under contract to CIRIA by W S Atkins Environment. Following CIRIA's usual practice, the research study was guided by a Steering Group.

STEERING GROUP

Mr J M McEntee (Chairman)	Consultant (formerly Wimpey Environmental Limited)
Dr D P Creedy	Wardell Armstrong (formerly of British Coal)
Mr M Da Rios	British Telecom World Wide Networks
Mr E J Farr	Northumbrian Environmental Management Ltd
Mr C Grant	Department of the Environment
Mr R J Ireland	North West Water
Mr A Lloyd	City of Birmingham
Mr N A Trenter	Sir William Halcrow and Partners

CIRIA's Research Managers for this project were Mr F M Jardine and Mr R Freer.

FUNDERS

The project was funded under Phase II of the programme *Methane and associated to construction* by:

Department of the Environment, Construction Directorate

Anglian Water Services Ltd

North West Water Ltd

Southern Water Services Ltd

Yorkshire Water Services Ltd

CIRIA Core Programme

ACKNOWLEDGEMENTS

CIRIA and W S Atkins Environment are grateful for help given to this project by the funders, by the members of the Steering Group and by the many individuals and organisation who were consulted.

Contents

Figures

Tables

Glossary

active gas control a method of controlling gas emission from a site using mechanical methods such as pumping and flaring and exhaust ventilation

anaerobic in the absence of oxygen

atmospheric temperature inversion the trapping of cold air at the ground surface below a stratified layer of warm air under certain, still, atmospheric conditions

basal containment the technique of sealing the base of a landfill with engineered natural materials and synthetic liners

BOD biochemical oxygen demand: a measure of the potential for a polluting liquid to remove oxygen from the receiving water by biological or biochemical oxidation processes

carbon reservoir the amount of carbon which is available to form carbon dioxide and methane

carbonaceous containing carbon

cellulose a long chain hydrocarbon found in all vegetable matter which can be broken down to many smaller compounds such as esters and alcohols and ultimately methane and carbon dioxide

COD chemical oxygen demand: a measure of the potential for a polluting liquid to remove oxygen from the receiving water by chemical oxidation processes (COD is always higher than BOD)

competent authority a local authority with a statutory interest (in the site investigation or development proposals)

COSHH Control of Substances Hazardous to Health: regulations specifically implemented to ensure the safe and proper handling and control of hazardous substances

desiccated dried (e.g. of an overlying capping or sealing layer, which shrinks and cracks on drying)

die-back the death of areas of vegetation due to, for example, methane displacing soil gas in the root zone

formal open space open (unbuilt) land given over to formal organised recreation (e.g. golf courses, football pitches)

gas chromatography an analytical technique which can be used to identify and quantify substances according to the relative rate at which they separate out when passed through a specific medium

general development order	regulations issued under the Town and and County Planning Act 1972 which, *inter alia*, require that any development within 250 m of a landfill should take due regard of the gas risk
hard development	development which involves buildings, paved areas and similar structures
hydrogeological	pertaining to the groundwater and its geological environment
hydrological	pertaining to the surface water environment
informal open space	open (unbuilt) land given over to informal use (e.g. parks and gardens)
intrinsically safe	of an instrument (or equipment) which does not generate an ignition source within the gas atmosphere being monitored (usually indicated by BSI accreditation)
leachate	polluting liquor produced by water percolating through wastes and leaching out contaminants
LEL	lower explosive limit; the minimum concentration in air at which methane can ignite (approximately 5%)
lignin	a complex polymer often found in association with cellulose
Loscoe	a village in Derbyshire where a house was destroyed by a landfill gas explosion in 1986
microbial	pertaining to micro-biological action
OEL	occupational exposure limit: the concentration of a substance, below which there is no evidence that it will be injurious to health for a specific time period of exposure
organic waste	waste which contains a significant proportion of carbonaceous materials and is thus degradable waste (e.g. vegetable matter)
out-gassing	the sudden release of dissolved gas from solution into the atmosphere
passive control	the control of gas emission by provision of engineered venting pathways (e.g. wells and vent trenches) without mechanical aid
pH	a measure of the acidity or alkalinity of a substance based on its hydrogen ion concentration
phytotoxic	being toxic to plant life
precipitation	rain, hail and snow
protocol	a formal statement of a logical or necessary sequence of actions to satisfy the objective underlying the need for these actions
putrescible	of something which will biodegrade
sensitive receptors	property and structures which are more likely to be affected by a gas hazard either by virtue of their location or construction

soft development	development which does not include buildings or other similar built structures (e.g. landscaping verges, open space)
standpipe	a rigid tube inserted into the ground which allows the sampling of gas and water (usually in a borehole)
stressed vegetation	vegetation which is dying or suffering from inhibited growth from the presence of landfill gas for example in the root zone
surface flux	the rate of gas emission through the ground surface
target situation	the specific circumstances of the receptors which are likely to receive any migrating gas
toxin	a toxic substance

1 Introduction

1.1 BACKGROUND

This report is part of CIRIA's continuing programme on *Methane and associated hazards to construction*. The programme is a response to concern that, in recent years, many developments have been constructed on or near sources of methane; while this is acceptable when appropriate precautions are taken, such precautions do not always appear to be based on consistent approaches to site investigation and hazard assessment.

In order to encourage a more consistent approach, CIRIA commissioned the following research projects and publications:

- A bibliography of some 500 references relating to the occurrence of methane at construction sites[1]
- A guidance document on the nature, origins and occurrence of methane[2]
- A guidance document on the methods of detection, sampling, measurement and monitoring of methane[3]
- A study to establish the priorities for research and information needed by the construction industry in relation to methane hazards[4]
- A guidance document about the protection of new and existing developments from methane and associated gases in the ground[5]
- The project reported here to establish policies and procedures for the selection of appropriate investigation methods and their implementation. A more detailed explanation of the objectives of this stage is given in Section 1.3.

Two other CIRIA reports from a further phase of the research address the interpretation of subsurface gas concentrations (Report 151) and the assessment of degrees of risk (Report 152).

1.2 HAZARDS OF METHANE AND ASSOCIATED GASES

Hooker and Bannon[2] describe in detail the hazards of methane, and gases that are likely to be associated with it, in the context of construction. A summary of the relevant characteristics of these gases is given below.

Methane (CH_4), which is most likely to be of landfill or mine origin, is a colourless, odourless gas whose principal hazard is that it is flammable (or explosive) when mixed with air in concentrations between approximately 5 and 15% by volume. The lower concentration is termed the Lower Explosive Limit (LEL) and it is sometimes convenient to refer to the measured gas concentration as a percentage of the LEL. It is important to stress that concentrations which fall outside the explosive limits are not to be considered safe, because concentrations may fluctuate widely over short timescales. Consequently these rapid fluctuations may periodically bring the gas concentration within its explosive range. The presence of other gases can, in some instances, affect the explosive range significantly, e.g. 5% methane plus 5% carbon dioxide in nitrogen is much less of an explosion hazard then 5% methane in air. Nevertheless from the general point of view of hazard assessment a concentration of 4.5% will not be considered less hazardous in practical terms than one of 5.5%.

Methane of landfill origin will usually be associated with carbon dioxide (CO_2), again an odourless and colourless gas. It can have a physiological effect on the respiratory system which is not solely related to its asphyxiating properties (i.e. the displacement of oxygen). The short-term (10 minutes) occupational exposure limit (OEL) for CO_2 is 1.5% by volume, and the long-term (8 hour) OEL is 0.5%[6].

Hydrogen sulphide (H_2S) can be evolved in significant quantities from landfill sites, where sulphate-containing materials such as plasterboard have been deposited, or from some colliery spoils. It is a highly toxic gas, with a short term OEL of 15 ppm and a long-term limit of 10 ppm. It is highly odorous, with a characteristic smell of rotten eggs, but it quickly desensitises the nasal nerves, so that a person may think the danger has passed when in fact it persists. The gas is also highly inflammable, with a lower explosive limit of 4.5% in air.

Carbon monoxide (CO) is a product of low temperature combustion. It is usually present in low concentrations in mine gases and some soil gases. Higher concentrations may arise in connection with combustion within landfills or abandoned mine workings. It is a colourless, almost odourless gas which is both highly toxic by inhalation and highly inflammable. Its occupational exposure limits are 300 ppm (short-term) and 50 ppm (long-term).

Other toxic gases which may be constituents of landfill gas or emitted by chemically contaminated ground or chemical waste deposits include hydrogen cyanide (HCN), phosphine (PH_3) and sulphur dioxide (SO_2). These are less commonly encountered in significant quantities than methane and carbon dioxide, but may be of crucial importance in individual cases and have to be taken into account at least at the initial appraisal stage of an investigation. Further information on the characteristics of these gases is given by Barry[7].

Regardless of its specific characteristics, any gas or mixture of gases may cause asphyxiation it if displaces oxygen in a confined space. An asphyxiation hazard exists if the oxygen content of air in the confined space falls below 18% by volume.

Gas-related hazards are relevant both to the construction process and to the long-term occupancy or other use of buildings and structures. Confined spaces in which hazardous conditions can arise include trenches, manholes, sewers and poorly ventilated spaces such as may be found below portable buildings, as well as within buildings themselves. A fundamental distinction to be drawn between gas hazards and other ground contamination issues is the relative ease and speed with which hazardous conditions can arise, and the potential consequences of an explosion especially within a building.

1.3   OBJECTIVES OF THE REPORT

It is apparent that methane investigations are often inadequate or inappropriate: sometimes needless work is called for; sometimes it is insufficient or addresses the wrong aspects. Investigations are, necessarily, specific to individual developments, but it appears that they vary considerably in degree, style and methods in a way which is not necessarily related to the nature of the development or the level of hazard anticipated. While there is substantial published guidance on the techniques available for gas detection, measurement and monitoring (including Reference 3), there is little or no guidance on the way in which these techniques should be combined, together with consultation, assessment and decision-making protocols, to establish an overall investigation strategy for a given development. Two relevant British Standards contain sound general guidance, BS 5930 : 1981 *Code of practice for site investigations*[8], and

Draft for Development 175 : 1988 *Code of practice for the identification of potentially contaminated land and its investigation*[9], but they are not sufficiently specific about methane and associated gases. Waste Management Paper 27 *Landfill Gas*[10] gives little information on decision-making procedures and is insufficiently focused on the requirements of new development.

In the light of increasing pressure for development on or near to marginal land, the gas hazards that may be associated with such development and the lack of detailed guidance, the purpose of this report is:

> to make known current good practice in the protocols, procedural stages and appropriate degrees or types of investigation for new or existing development sites where methane and associated gases may be present.

1.4   STATEMENT OF APPROACH

A study of procedures currently in use in the UK was carried out by means of direct interviews with selected practitioners in the field of gas hazard assessment, supplemented by interviews and correspondence with other interested parties and reference to specific case histories and published literature.

The practitioners who were consulted were from both public and private sector organisations, principally consultants and waste regulation authorities. The interested parties whose advice was sought included planning, waste regulation, environmental health and building control authorities; developers; building contractors; building societies and other funding agencies, and insurers: a full list is included in Appendix A.

Interviews with practitioners had a two-fold purpose : (a) to determine the practitioners' views and working practices with regard to investigation strategies, and (b) to identify specific case histories as a basis for investigating the views of other parties. The other interested parties were interviewed to obtain their overall views on, and expectations of, the investigation procedures.

The findings of these investigations are set out in the report, together with recommendations for good practice and indications of where practice is yet to be improved. This report is intended to give guidance which will allow the reader to identify an investigation scenario of interest, which can then be tailored to the specific context of the site being considered. Perhaps of equal importance is helping to prevent the selection of inappropriate investigation strategies.

2 Objectives of gas investigations

The ultimate objective of all investigations, as viewed by landowners, scheme promoters or regulators, should be identical, namely to ensure that a proposed development may take place safely, with appropriate precautions taken, and remain safe. However, this is not to assume that there is a consensus among interested parties on the methods required to achieve that objective, particularly with regard to the level of detail which may be required of information at different stages of an investigation, or for different gas sources or types of development. Set out below is an explanation of the way in which, in principle, investigation requirements may vary in different circumstances. The succeeding sections of the report take account of these possible variations and the extent to which they apply in practice.

The gas investigation itself comprises a variety of investigative techniques applied in a logical sequence, covering the site and its surroundings and usually a specific part of the site, for sampling and analysis of the gas regime within the groundmass over a period of time. The specific components of the site investigation and the way in which they are combined will be determined mainly by two conditions:

1. The development or project context : i.e. the circumstances of the target situation or potential receptors which necessitate a gas investigation and risk assessment (e.g. proposed development).

2. The perceived gas hazard : i.e. the nature of the gas source and the way in which the risk to potential receptors is manifested.

Both conditions, in turn, are influenced by a wide variety of factors, as indicated in Figure 2.1. Because of the complexity and variety of interrelationships between these factors, each of the two main determinants above is illustrated in further detail in Figures 2.2 and 2.3 respectively.

2.1 PERCEIVED GAS HAZARD

2.1.1 Gas generation factors

Origin of the gas

The major influence that the origin of the gas has on the perceived gas hazard is in relation to the potential for continued and significant gas production. Gas originating from a landfill site represents a present source of production, and any gas vented to atmosphere will be quickly replaced. Gas from natural, geological sources, e.g. gas-bearing strata, peat and silt generally represents a historical source, the gas from which has remained trapped below ground, but which when vented will not be replaced by active gas production. The initial volumes, however, may be great and thus gas may be present for a very long time.

Groundwater, while not in itself a source of gas, may be a carrier of dissolved gas. At normal pressure and temperature the solubility of methane in groundwater is very low. However, under high pressures, significant volumes of gas may dissolve in groundwater, and thus are capable of being transported over long distances. Out-gassing will occur on release of the pressure, e.g. where tunnelling excavations or piled surface structures encounter such groundwater and thus allow an interface with the atmosphere. Rising groundwater levels may influence gas generation by increasing the moisture content in hitherto dry zones of the landfill.

Dimensions of the gas source

The potential gas risk is influenced by the volumes of gas involved, a function of both the rate of gas generation and the volume of the gas source. The larger the gas producing body, the greater the volumes, and thus the greater potential sphere of influence of the gas body. Of particular importance is the depth of the gas source. For landfill gas sources the greater the depth, the more likely it is that anaerobic, and thus methane generating, conditions will prevail. Also, for gas sources generally, the greater the depth, the greater the potential for lateral subsurface migration.

The age of the gas source is not necessarily an influence, but for landfill sites in particular it will give an indication of the potential for gas generation. More recent waste deposits (since the Clean Air Acts 1956 and 1968) typically contain a higher proportion of biodegradable matter than earlier deposits which comprised mainly ash and glass and were thus of low gas generation potential.

Rate of gas generation

Methane is generated by microbial activity on carbonaceous matter, and so the total gas quantity depends on the size of the carbon reservoir (potential or actual). The total carbon reservoir in a landfill will influence the potential lifetime of gas generation, and may indicate that the potential exists for gas generation even if it is not occurring at present.

As the majority of modern gas generation occurs by microbial activity any influence on this activity will alter the rate of generation. Generally environmental conditions such as temperature, moisture content, pH and nutrient and toxin levels may influence the rate of gas generation. Gas production may follow a yearly cycle, increasing in summer and decreasing in winter, because of significant seasonal variations in temperature in particular.

2.1.2   Gas migration factors

Meteorological conditions

The rate of fall of atmospheric pressure is more significant than the actual pressure level in influencing gas emission rates. Rapidly falling pressure can lead to a pressure differential between the gas body and the atmosphere in general, thus providing a motive force for gas emission. Once equilibrium of pressure has been reached, even at low barometric pressure, the motive force is removed and the influence of barometric pressure on potential gas migration is greatly reduced.

Precipitation can lead to a reduction in the permeability of the ground surface by sealing migration routes, again leading to a build-up of pressure within a gas body, and the potential for an increase in subsurface migration.

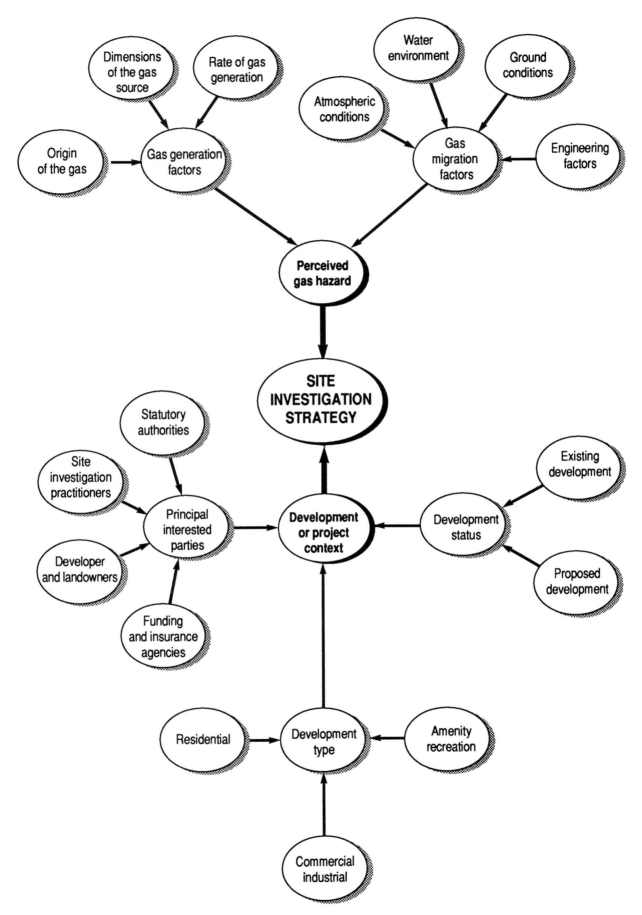

Figure 2.1 Potential influences on a site investigation strategy

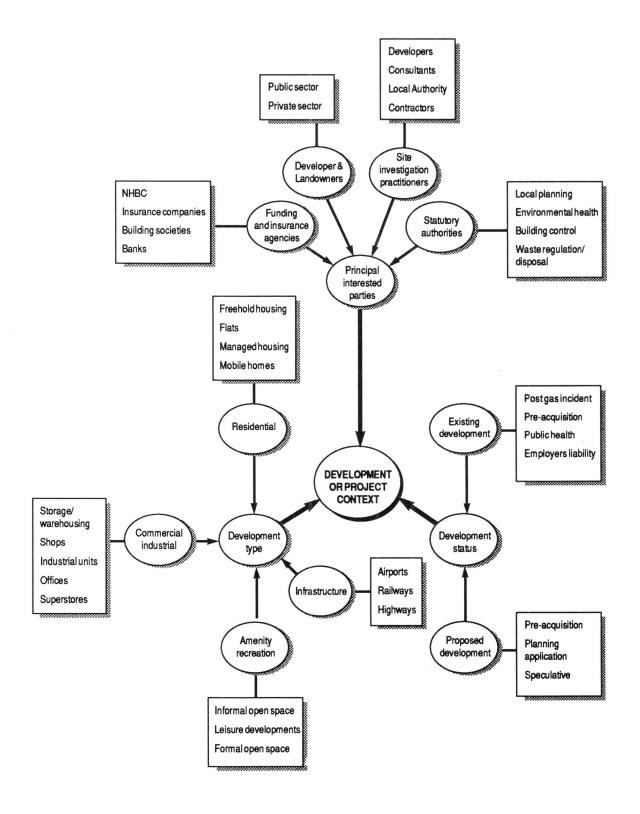

Figure 2.2 Factors influencing the development or project context

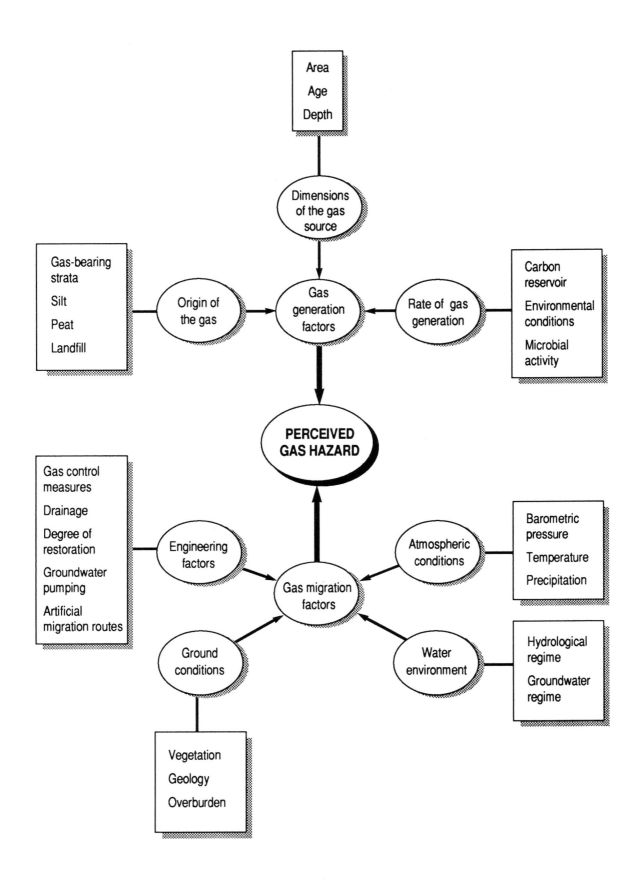

Figure 2.3 Factors influencing the perception of gas hazard

The influence of temperature on gas migration potential is generally considered to be of less importance. However, during periods of high atmospheric pressures and still conditions, an atmospheric temperature inversion could lead to a situation in which gas vented from the ground surface is not rapidly dispersed, but may accumulate in hollows or other depressions.

Ground conditions

The geology of the ground surrounding the gas source is of particular significance to potential gas migration in that it influences the number and accessibility of natural gas migration pathways, whether laterally or towards the surface. In the case of landfill, the nature of the cover has a similar influence. Some soils can oxidise methane to carbon dioxide, an exothermic process which can give rise to a considerable temperature increase.

Water environment

Changes in groundwater conditions may influence the gas regime in terms of both gas generation and gas migration. In particular, a rise in groundwater levels within or below the gas source material may lead to an increase in gas pressure, and hence there may be an increase in lateral subsurface migration. Surface water features (e.g. rivers, canals) may, under certain circumstances, provide barriers to lateral migration.

Engineering factors

Engineering factors may provide a variety of influences on the gas regime. The presence of any gas control measures may have a beneficial influence, reducing the potential gas risk. The presence of pipelines, sewers, land drains, and other buried services may provide artificial preferential migration pathways. Pumping which lowers groundwater levels (e.g. during quarrying), may also influence the gas regime by opening new migration paths. Cessation of pumping may have the same effect as naturally rising groundwater levels.

2.2 DEVELOPMENT OR PROJECT CONTEXT

2.2.1 Development type

Residential

Of importance with regard to residential property may be whether the corporate development is freehold or managed. On managed developments there will be some measure of control or prohibition of the erection of small surface structures (such as garden sheds and greenhouses) which are unlikely to have the same degree of gas exclusion or protection as the main building; this is highly unlikely to be the case on freehold developments so there is a possibility that on freehold sites the occupants could place themselves at greater risk of a gas incident by erecting such structures. The design and form of the structure is also of importance in terms of its vulnerability to gas ingress.

For developments comprising mobile homes, one of the main aspects to be considered is the void space between the ground surface and the floor.

Commercial/Industrial

Commercial and industrial developments may include a range of built structures such as shops, offices, superstores, storage/warehousing and a variety of industrial units. The use of these buildings will usually be reflected in their size and internal structure, and it is these factors that will be of importance with regard to the development or project context. These types of development will almost always involve areas of hardstanding (e.g. car parks), perhaps most significantly in connection with superstores and other shopping developments.

Infrastructure

Infrastructure developments, such as highways and associated services, have the potential to provide linear man-made migration pathways, and thus may extend the sphere of influence of a gas body well beyond its immediate environs. Other influences are related to the possible sealing of ground surfaces, thus altering, in particular, the venting characteristics of a gas regime.

Amenity/recreation

An amenity/recreation development will often involve areas of open space. These may include areas of hard surface cover (car parks, paved areas, hard tennis courts, etc.), as well as soft landscaped areas. These open spaces may involve formal uses (e.g. sports fields, golf courses) or be for informal use (e.g. wildlife sanctuaries). These developments will often include a variety of buildings, ranging in size from small cabins/huts (e.g. ticket offices, toilet blocks) to large buildings (e.g. leisure centres, exhibition halls). The proportions of the various components of the development may have an influence on the site investigation strategy.

2.2.2 Development status

Proposed development

For a proposed development a gas investigation may be called for at different stages, e.g. during site selection, prior to finalising the acquisition of a site, or as a consequence of the planning application. The stage at which the investigation is carried out may dictate the extent of information required and hence the necessary investigation strategy.

Existing development

For an existing development a gas investigation may be required prior to the sale or purchase of the site, particularly in relation to provision of insurance cover or warranties to cover future liabilities, or to ensure the health and safety of the occupants or workforce. Investigation may be required in other situations where there is a perceived risk to public health in general. The necessity for an investigation is almost certain following a gas-related incident.

2.2.3 Principal interested parties

Although all parties concerned with the development of gas risk sites have the same principal objective – safe construction and occupancy of the site – there are other aspects of the investigation that may be influenced by the specific interests of the different parties.

Statutory authorities

The statutory authorities that are likely to have an interest in the results of a gas investigation include the Local Planning Authority, the Environmental Health Department, and the Building Control Authority. Also, although the Waste Regulation Authority (WRA) may not be directly involved, it is often consulted as a source of expert advice by the aforementioned authorities. Where a development site lies within 250 m of a landfill that was operational within the previous 30 years, the WRA must be consulted under the Town and County Planning General Development Order 1988.

The authorities have a duty to ensure that the investigation is adequate for its purposes and complies with current guidance as, once the development is authorised, the authorities could be answerable to the public for any problems that arise through inadequate assessment of the risk.

Statutory authorities may also be involved as developers, e.g. development corporations, particularly with respect to reclaiming derelict land and making it suitable for development.

Site investigation practitioners

The responsibility for site investigation can be undertaken by various parties. These may include specialist consultants, local authority departments, or the developers themselves, or their appointed contractors. In general most site investigations are likely to be undertaken by specialist consultants, commissioned by landowners or prospective developers. Local authorities will principally be involved with gas investigations on sites of existing development where there is a perceived gas risk to the public or on land owned by the authority which is earmarked for future development.

Developers and landowners

The investigations may be required either by the landowner or the developer, whether from the public or private sector. The main public sector involvement is likely to be where a gas source presents a hazard to existing site occupiers. Where there may be an immediate danger to the site occupiers, the investigation is likely to be intense and concentrated to maximise the amount of data of the gas regime in as short a time period as possible. Financial considerations are unlikely to be a constraint in this instance. Private sector developers, typically, would require an investigation as a prerequisite for gaining authorisation for their development, notwithstanding their responsibility to ensure that the proposed development will be safe. They are likely to adopt a cost effective, phased investigation, designed to provide sufficient information for the authorities and themselves to be confident that adequate mitigation measures can be incorporated into the proposed development, and thus ensure the safety of future occupiers. Costs may cause developers to abandon a scheme or they may adopt maximum safety measures rather than continuing with a detailed investigation, assuming the worst case.

Funding and insurance agencies

Other agencies that may be interested in the strategy and findings of a gas investigation include banks and building societies, who may be funding the development, and insurance companies and the National House-Building Council (NHBC), who may be required to give warranties with regard to potential future liabilities. They need to feel confident that the buildings are safe and robust and will remain so; they do not like to rely on contingency measures for future remedial works should things go wrong.

3   Investigation techniques

A detailed description and discussion of techniques for investigating and monitoring gases in the ground is given by Crowhurst and Manchester[3]. The following summary is based on that source together with other current information.

3.1   GAS MONITORING INSTALLATIONS

Table 3.1 summarises the techniques that are available to produce wells or points from which samples or measurements can be taken. The appropriateness of the techniques to the different stages and types of investigation that may arise is discussed in Section 6.

* Several factors affect the choice of investigation techniques to be used. These are:
* depth considerations, based on depth to (a) source (if known), (b) gas-permeable strata, and (c) development excavations
* access problems
* existing information on the site history, geology and hydrogeology.

3.2   GAS MONITORING INSTRUMENTS

Once the monitoring installations have been put in place and allowed a satisfactory rest period (which will be site specific), sampling of the gas regime can commence. There are two principal methods:

1. *In-situ* testing using a portable field instrument.
2. Laboratory analysis of sample collected in a suitable receptacle.

3.2.1   Portable instruments

Most investigations would utilise both of the above methods to varying degrees, although it is likely that the use of field instruments will predominate in the majority of investigations. The various characteristics of field instruments are described in Table 3.2.

The most commonly used and proven devices are the combined thermal conductivity/catalytic oxidation devices (often incorporating an electrochemical cell for oxygen determination) and more recently infra-red analysers (again incorporating an oxygen detector).

The latter devices allow the monitoring of methane, carbon dioxide and oxygen simultaneously. The former type of device, however, although not capable of identifying carbon dioxide, is the only type certified as being intrinsically safe in flammable gas environments although not all devices are so certified. This, of course, is of critical importance where the device is to be used in a confined space such as a service access or building. The alternative is to use a remote sampling probe or to take samples in tubes for later analysis.

Table 3.1 Types of gas monitoring installation

Method	Advantages	Drawbacks
Spiking; metal spike pushed into the ground and removed, creating hole from which a sample can be taken	– very quick, cheap, easy to use	– maximum depth 1m – very poor accuracy – hole may become blocked – confirms gas presence but not absence
Shallow probes; hollow rigid perforated pipe, sealed at top with connection to gas detection device, pushed into the ground	– quick, cheap, easy to install	– maximum depth 2 m unless special tubes used – perforations can become blocked – as for spiking, can only indicate gas present
Auger; a hand held auger with extendable sections is used to bore into the ground	– cheap and simple to use – allows sampling of solids – deeper than spiking/shallow probes	– physically difficult – cannot penetrate difficult ground – can be time consuming
Driven probes; hollow casing tube with solid nose-cone is driven into the ground mechanically, monitoring pipe installed inside the casing, casing extracted leaving nose-cone behind	– minimal ground disturbance – light, easily portable machinery thus access problems unlikely – normal maximum depth 10 m	– will not penetrate obstructions
Trial pits; a wheeled or tracked mechanical excavator is used to create a pit, or trench, into which a perforated standpipe is installed, and the pit backfilled with the arisings	– relatively quick and cheap – allows visual inspection of the sample strata and assessment of the bulk characteristics of the ground during excavation and can therefore form part of main ground investigation	– maximum depth 5-6 m – causes ground disturbance (must allow longer stabilisation periods) – backfilled material may allow venting – may cause a hazard to public health and a danger to persons on site – possible access problems – depth may be limited by instability – brings contaminated material to the surface
Boreholes (cable-percussive); a cased borehole is sunk by cable percussive techniques into which a perforated standpipe is installed with gravel surround, and the casing withdrawn	– great depths attainable – minimal disturbance to ground – can install several standpipes in one borehole to monitor different levels – can inspect and sample strata during boring and can therefore form part of main ground investigation – can use to monitor groundwater	– relatively slow and expensive – may have access problems (needs large working area) – brings contaminated material to the surface
Boreholes (rotary); similar to above but the hole is drilled by a rotary tool and flushed with air or water: essential for hard rock penetration, e.g. for investigation of cavities and old mine workings	– as above, but quicker than cable percussion technique (especially air flush), – relatively mobile rig (fixed body vehicle)	– as above, but also air flush method does not prevent sparking, thus potentially hazardous on gassing site – water flush can spread contamination
Surface sampling (flux boxes); an inverted container is emplaced on the site surface and any gas collected is sampled through a valve	– gives an indication of emission rates – cheap and easy to install – non-intrusive	– box is easily disturbed – value of the information obtained is not certain

Table 3.2 Portable gas monitoring instruments

Detector type	Characteristics	Comments
Catalytic oxidation	– detects presence of any flammable gas, even at low concentrations – cannot distinguish gases – cannot be used where O_2 less than 12 to 15% by volume – basic type gives erroneous results for gas concentrations above upper explosive limit (UEL) – catalyst may be poisoned by minor constituents of some vapours	These two devices are often combined in the same instrument; the catalytic oxidation detector is typically used for measuring gas concentrations from 0-100% LEL, while the thermal conductivity device is used for measuring concentrations from 0–100% gas in air
Thermal conductivity	– can detect concentrations up to 100% by volume – is easily combined with other detectors – inaccurate where composition of two or more gases in equal quantity, depending on which gases present – poor resolution at low concentrations	
Flame ionisation	– very sensitive (0-10 000 ppm), can be used in open air – not suitable where O_2 is low – responds to any combustible gas or vapours – dangerous in an explosive area – sample destroyed by sensor	This device is not intrinsically safe. Erroneous readings arise in presence of significant CO_2 Cross-sensitivity with hydrocarbons. Poor resolution at low concentrations with methane
Infra-red analysers	– useful for wide range of gases – wide and sensitive detection range – selection of measuring wavelength difficult – readings affected by water in sample	Principally used for the detection of CH_4 and CO_2. Typically they are not intrinsically safe. Cross-sensitivity with hydrocarbons. Poor resolution at low concentrations with CH_4
Electrochemical cell	– can be used to detect a wide variety of gases – cell has limited life span – can be poisoned by certain gases	Mainly used to detect O_2 and often combined with catalytic oxidation/thermal conductivity devices
Paramagnetic sensors	– used for the detection of oxygen	
Chemical detector tubes	– used for a wide variety of gases – wide detection range – may be useful for measurement of toxic contaminants	– low accuracy – time consuming
Semi-conductors	– not easily poisoned – can be made very sensitive	

Typically, these instruments will be used where significant concentrations of gas are expected during routine monitoring of the gas monitoring installations. The use of a flame ionisation detector is only appropriate for monitoring for low or trace levels of gas where the other instruments have failed to detect any, e.g. where gas is venting to the atmosphere at the site surface, such that dilution is so rapid that the concentrations present are below the detection limit of the other instruments.

It is important to note when monitoring for methane that, although the instruments are calibrated to give a measured response to methane concentration (i.e. 5% methane concentration will cause a deflection of the needle or monitoring display to read 5%), the detector is actually measuring flammable gas and will record any flammable gas. It is possible, therefore that under certain circumstances, e.g. where fuel or organic solvent contamination is present, the instrument will give erroneous methane readings. Instruments should be calibrated regularly.

Measurement of emission rates

An important factor in assessing the gas regime is the apparent emission rate of the gas from the source. This must obviously be measured *in situ* and as such must involve portable instruments. Actual emission measurement, however, is more complicated than for concentration, and to date there are no fully reliable or proven techniques. The principal techniques currently used are described in Table 3.3. Pressure measurements using micromanometers may also be used as a general indication of emission potential, but can be less satisfactory than direct volume measurements.

Table 3.3 Emission rate measurement techniques

Technique	Description	Limitations
Direct measurement	– volume flow rate is measured directly from the monitoring point by devices such as rotameters, vane anemometers or bubble-flow meters. The simplest method involves the collection of a volume of gas over water in a measured time	– can only be used where gas quantity and pressure are high – calibration is affected by the density, temperature and pressure of the gas mixture – tends to underestimate because of back pressure reducing flow if collection over water
Hot-wire anemometer	– a thermal conductivity device measures the gas velocity from the monitoring point; if its cross sectional area is known the emission rate can be calculated using conversion charts from air to gas mixtures	– changes in composition of the gas stream during measurement will give spurious results – emission velocity is affected by introducing the device to the gas stream – easily influenced by cross wind, and hand vibration
Re-circulation	– the borehole is flushed with an inert gas and then cycled through a concentration monitoring device; the rate of change of concentration can be used (along with the volume of the borehole) to calculate the recharge and hence potential emission rate	– can only be used where emission rate is very low – gross assumptions and sampling error make the results doubtful – only suitable for boreholes designed for this purpose
Micromanometer	– typically comprises a device with a transducer and two sample lines, one registers atmospheric pressure, the other registers the relative pressure at the sample point	– Cannot be related directly to an emission rate

3.2.2   Laboratory analysis of gas samples

An alternative or supplementary method to using portable field instruments for analysing the gas regime is to collect a gas sample from the monitoring installation for analysis in a laboratory, either by gas chromatography (GC) or by less costly infra-red (IR) analyses.

Samples can be taken by the use of evacuated sample cylinders, Gresham tubes, syringes and other such devices. A more detailed account is given in Crowhurst and Manchester[3]. It is important to monitor the gas being sampled during its collection, either to corroborate the laboratory results or to confirm the accuracy of the field instrument. It is preferable for the gas monitoring instrument to be in parallel with the collection device, but if this is not possible it should be placed 'downstream' of the collecting device. If placed upstream, is is essential that the monitoring instrument is non-destructive, (i.e. does not destroy or alter the gas sample).

The main advantages of gas chromatographic analysis are:
- gas can be determined qualitatively and quantitatively
- a wide range of gases can be analysed, including trace constituents
- the results can be very accurate
- an expensive, intrinsically safe instrument is not required.

There are, however, some drawbacks to the use of GC, the principal ones being:
- equipment and analysis are highly specialised and very expensive (in many cases low cost laboratory analysis is sufficient)
- the value of the results is totally dependent upon the competence of the sampling method (where some sampling errors can be large) as with on-site measurement
- the equipment is often non-portable.

Given the cost and logistical implications of analysing by gas chromatography, and the fact that resolving gas levels to the accuracy available with GC is not usually necessary, the predominant use of this technique is to confirm the accuracy of the field instruments periodically and to clarify anomalous results, e.g. the technique will also indicate if other flammable gases are present.

Laboratory analysis of gas samples is essential where it is necessary to identify the source of the gas. Depending upon the specific circumstances, the gas source might be identifiable from either its age or its composition. Analysis of gas composition may allow distinctions to be made between mains gas and landfill gas, or landfill gas and gas of geological origin. This is typically done by GC, but will often include the use of mass spectrometry (MS) to give an accurate identification of trace gases, which may be indicative of a specific gas source. This may not be possible where there is a mixture of gases from different sources.

Carbon 14 dating, radiometric dating, mass spectrometric dating and stable isotope measurements can each all be used to help identify the age of the gas, and thus distinguish, for example, between landfill or marsh gas and geological gas from mines or gas mains. More information about these techniques is given in References 2 and 3.

Techniques for determining the age and composition of a gas in order to define its source, all require specialist equipment and interpretation and are therefore expensive. Nevertheless, adequate knowledge of the source or sources is a critical factor in designing the most effective monitoring and control techniques.

3.3 ADDITIONAL TECHNIQUES

An additional method of assessing the potential for gas production in landfill sites is to take samples of the waste and analyse them to determine the ratio of cellulose to lignin. As waste degradation proceeds the cellulose to lignin ratio decreases. In theory, therefore, it is possible to determine, broadly, the stage of decomposition and thus indicate the remaining gassing potential of the site. This can also be attempted by comparing the COD to BOD ratio in leachates: a higher ratio is indicative of more advanced degradation. These techniques are subject to a large degree of uncertainty and sampling variations. They should only be used, therefore, in support of direct measurements of the gas regime.

Where an attempt is being made to identify leaks or define migration pathways, for example, in mine workings or service runs, then tracer studies can be used to 'label' the gas and identify it at a subsequent location. This, however, is not a commonly used technique.

4 Review of current procedures

One of the main tasks of this CIRIA project was to identify current good practice in the design and execution of investigation procedures for sites potentially at risk from methane and associated gases. This research comprised three principal stages:

1. Literature review of current national guidance on site investigations and methane hazard assessment.

2. Review of current good practices of site investigation as employed by experienced practitioners.

3. Review of site investigation procedures expected by the statutory authorities and the information requirements of both these and other principal interested parties, such as developers, funders and insurers.

The results of this research are discussed in detail later in this section and are illustrated with suitable case histories where appropriate. The main findings of the research are summarised below.

4.1 SUMMARY OF FINDINGS

The study of current practice showed that, while there is some consistency in the approach to, and the practice of, site investigations among the practitioners consulted, this is often incompatible with the expectations of the statutory authorities.

The lack of specific detailed guidance on site investigation strategies, and the wide range in experience between practitioners and statutory authorities, has led to a large degree of inconsistency in the standards applied to or expected of site investigations.

In general, many authorities responsible for permitting new development appear to apply a rigid interpretation of existing guidance when specifying what they require of a site investigation or subsequent risk mitigation measures. The main reasons for this appear to be ambiguous and inconsistent guidance, a lack of specific experience or understanding of the nature of the hazards posed by methane, or previous experience of inappropriate developments and inadequate site investigations on potential gas risk sites.

Amongst experienced practitioners and some local authorities there is a general consensus on the principal elements of a site investigation strategy, namely

- desk study and walk-over survey
- preliminary site investigation (employing shallow and/or deep techniques)
- detailed site investigation (i.e. expansion of the preliminary investigation again using shallow and/or deep techniques as appropriate)
- long-term, regular monitoring and supplementary investigation as necessary.

It is important to stress that the above is a generalised strategy; not all investigations need all of the above steps, nor necessarily in the sequence shown, although it is likely that most would. All parties interviewed for this research emphasised that each case is site specific and that there can be no rigid format applied to all site investigations. Furthermore, all parties agreed that specific guidance on site investigation procedures was urgently needed in the light of the inconsistency and lack of specificity of current official publications.

The other principal interested parties in the investigation of potential methane risk sites are developers, insurers and funding agencies. The developers' stated main requirement for a site investigation is that it satisfies the competent authority that the proposed or existing development is, and will remain, safe either by virtue of the gas regime present or through the installation of effective gas control or exclusion measures. Similarly the funding agencies for new developments, who provide money to either the developers or prospective purchasers, require that the level of risk be defined such that they can be confident the development or property is not materially affected by the gas risk and will therefore not lose value or result in substantial liabilities. The insurance sector emphasised that they must be satisfied that the likely occurrence of an incident involving methane or associated gases is minimal and thus acceptable. Based on their actual experience of such incidents resulting in claims (principally Loscoe) the risk, in the context of all other risks that may affect developments, is of low incidence and not of major concern to the insurers at present, although the situation is under observation.

From the research undertaken it was possible to identify the problem areas *vis à vis* uncertainties and inconsistencies that currently exist in the execution of methane site investigations and assessments. Furthermore, a series of appropriate strategies has been formulated from the findings of this research which are *indicative* of the procedures appropriate to a particular scenario (see Sections 5 and 6). The research findings are discussed in detail below.

4.2   LITERATURE REVIEW

There have been a number of Department of the Environment (DoE) publications in recent years relating to methane and its potential hazards to development and the public. These are:

- Waste Management Paper No. 26, *Landfilling Wastes* (1986) (currently being updated)
- DoE Circular 21/87, *Development of Contaminated Land* (1987)
- Building Research Establishment Report, *Measurement of Gas Emissions from Contaminated Land* (1987)
- DoE Circular 17/89, *Landfill Sites – Development Control* (1989)
- Interdepartmental Committee on the Redevelopment of Contaminated Land, *Notes on the Development and After-use of Landfill Sites* (1990)
- Waste Management Paper No. 27, *Landfill Gas* (1989, 2nd Edition 1991)
- Building Research Establishment Report, *Construction of New Buildings on Gas Contaminated Land* (1991)
- Building Regulations Approved Document C,
- *Site Preparation and Resistance to Moisture* (1985, revised 1992).

In addition to these, the BSI publications Draft for Development DD175: 1988, *Code of Practice for the Identification of Potentially Contaminated Land and its Investigation*, and BS 5930:1981, *Code of Practice for Site Investigations*, are of particular relevance, as is the Institute of Wastes Management's *Monitoring of Landfill Gas* (1989). There are of course numerous other 'unofficial' publications by various authors, including the CIRIA publications which form part of this series and Special Publication 78 *Building on derelict land* (Leach and Goodger, 1991). For the purpose of this report the discussion will concentrate on the official government publications (the most recent editions) as it is typically within the context of these that the relevant regulatory authorities set their requisite criteria for site investigations.

All the documents listed above were quoted by the majority of parties consulted as being the best guidance currently available and used.

4.2.1 Waste Management Paper No. 26, *Landfilling Wastes* (1986)

This publication (WMP26) predominantly relates to the design, operation and restoration of landfill sites. There is, however, specific reference to site investigation and development of closed landfills. The main points of relevance are:

1. Difficulties with building on recently completed landfills may be extremely expensive to overcome but shallow landfills over 20 years old may be suitable for development subject to detailed assessment.

2. A site investigation, following a desk study, should involve the use of trial pits to reveal the nature, composition and likely variability of the fill, and boreholes to provide information on water levels in the refuse and gas emission rates.

3. The assessment, in addition to geotechnical factors, should consider the possibility of chemical attack, gas and leachate generation, combustibility and toxicity.

4. Only designs which will ensure the safety of the buildings and their occupants until gas is no longer being produced – possibly 50 years – should be used.

Although WMP 26 contains other references to site investigation procedures these relate to sites to be developed as landfill facilities and, thus, gas risk to development is not an issue. Insofar as the document provides general advice and information on some of the technical aspects of landfilling and its pollution potential, the document is only of background value for planning investigations. The only specific guidance is that given above.

4.2.2 DoE Circular 21/87, *Development of Contaminated Land* (1987)

This Circular is intended to provide guidance and advice to local authorities and developers on the identification, assessment and development of contaminated land. The guidance, however, is very general but although principally aimed at local authorities developers can draw clear inferences (see point 7 below for example). The salient points of the Circular are:

1. A balance has to be struck between the risks and liabilities associated with developing contaminated sites and the need to bring the land back into beneficial use.

2. The specific policies and practices to be adopted by local planning authorities are for authorities themselves to decide given the particular local circumstances in their areas.

3. Contamination, or the potential for it, is a material planning consideration.

4. Very few sites are so badly contaminated that they cannot be reused at all, but the choice of new use may be partially restricted by the contamination.

5. Each site must be considered on its own merits and if necessary treated with caution.

6. The responsibility for assessing whether or not land is suitable for a particular purpose rests primarily with the developer.

7. The responsibility for safe development and secure occupancy of the site rests with the developer.

8. When it is known or strongly suspected that the site is contaminated to an extent which would adversely affect the proposed development, an investigation by the developer to identify any remedial measures for dealing with the hazards will normally be required before the planning applications can be decided.

9. Where there is only a suspicion that the site might be contaminated or where the evidence suggests that there is potentially only slight contamination, planning permission may be granted with the condition that a site investigation and assessment should be carried out and necessary mitigation measures adopted in the development.

10. The local planning authority may grant planning permission without specific contamination conditions where there are reasonable grounds to believe none are required.

11. The assessment of the significance of contamination and of the associated risks requires careful professional judgement (local planning authorities should obtain advice from other local government experts).

12. Building regulations approval should not be refused unless the contamination would directly affect the building or structure or the health and safety of occupiers and users of the buildings.

Although gas is not referred to specifically in the Circular, investigation for methane and associated gases is relevant to the assessment of contaminated land, and thus the above points are applicable. Again, however, the guidance is not specific to site investigation procedures and strategies.

4.2.3 BRE, *Measurement of Gas Emissions from Contaminated Land* (1987)

This publication gives specific guidance on site investigation procedures, principally in the context of methane emissions from landfill presenting a risk to development and the health risk posed by carbon dioxide.

The document illustrates which techniques and parameters are considered appropriate to an adequate investigation strategy for situations where gas may present a risk to development. It is stated that an investigation would normally be required under the following circumstances:

- redevelopment on or adjacent to a former landfill site which has taken organic wastes
- where nuisance such as die-back or odours occur on or adjacent to a landfill
- following fires and explosions resulting from landfill gas emissions
- redevelopment of sites potentially at risk from other sources of gas of biological origin (e.g. marshy areas and river sides)
- where assessment of the viability of gas utilisation is needed.

The guidance, on the whole, is general and discussive rather than specific; however, there are a number of clear recommendations on specific factors in a site investigation. These can be summarised as follows:

1. Measurements should be made of gas composition, concentration and emission, and atmospheric conditions should be recorded whenever possible.

2. The aim of a preliminary assessment should be to confirm the presence of gas and should include testing for gas at the site periphery.

3. Subsurface examination of the whole site should be carried out where little or no surface emission is detected. Steel probes and trial pits may suffice for this purpose.

4. In all cases of hard development further more detailed investigation is required.

5. Data from the preliminary assessment should be used to identify the areas of the site requiring detailed investigation.

6. The detailed investigation should characterise the areas of significant gas emission in terms of composition, concentration and emission of gas and their relationship with climatic and ground conditions.

7. Monitoring should occur over several months before and during development of the site.

8. Spatial distribution of sampling points should reflect the proposed development and thus be concentrated in the areas designated for hard development and relatively high gas presence. A uniform grid pattern is only appropriate to the preliminary assessment.

9. Continual monitoring of the whole site is essential throughout the development programme.

10. Permanent or long-term monitoring will require the installation of boreholes. Trial pits are a satisfactory addition to borehole investigation.

These recommendations, however, are not put into the perspective of possible development scenarios, i.e. they are in the form of broad indicative guidance. As such they would have to be developed for each specific situation.

The report provides useful detail in relation to specific monitoring techniques and equipment. Much of this, however, is updated in the report by Crowhurst and Manchester[3] for the CIRIA methane programme (these authors being from the Fire Research Station of the Building Research Establishment).

4.2.4   DoE Circular 17/89, *Landfill Sites : Development Control* (1989)

This Circular states that if local planning authorities and developers heed the guidance given therein and in Waste Management Papers No: 4, 26 and 27, then account will have been taken of the risk to the development from landfill gas migration.

With respect to site investigation for landfill gas, however, there is only one specific reference, i.e.

> Where the presence of gas has been discovered or it is suspected
> that it may be present during the development of a site,
> investigations should be carried out to determine the source of the
> gas and apply any remedial measures to prevent it causing a hazard
> either during the course of the development or during subsequent
> use of the site. In this context, developers and planning authorities
> should be aware of Circular 21/87, Waste Management Paper No
> 27 and the Guidance Notes of the Interdepartmental Committee on
> the Redevelopment of Contaminated Land (ICRCL).

The rest of the Circular discusses the general principles of development control with respect to landfill sites.

4.2.5 ICRCL 17/78, *Notes on the Development and After-use of Landfill Sites* (8th Edition – 1990)

This guidance note was prepared to provide advice to parties considering the development of former landfill sites and deals with gas, toxic and geotechnical problems associated with such development. Advice is given on planning and control aspects, site assessment requirements and remedial measures.

With respect to the site assessment, the guidance note states that a detailed site investigation should always be carried out unless comprehensive knowledge of the site history and ground conditions already exists, except for some low-grade end uses (e.g. car parking). Furthermore, the scope of the investigation should be determined by the proposed end use and the principal hazards likely to affect that use.

More specifically a site investigation for development on a landfill site should comprise the following components:

- examination of available maps, plans, aerial photographs and other records (e.g. site licences)
- site visit to confirm documentary evidence with the actual conditions and identify potential problem areas
- a systematic ground survey using sample locations based on a grid pattern (spaced in accordance with DD175). Typical grid spacings of 10, 25, 50 or 100 m may be used depending upon the size of the site or area under examination
- solid samples should be taken from trial pits or boreholes at varying depths and testing carried out for toxic, asphyxiant and flammable gases
- the extent and scope of analyses should be tailored to the sensitivity of the end use of the site. For the construction of buildings this should include:
  - emission of toxic and flammable gases;
  - chemical attack on construction materials and subsidence;
  - human health effects on site workers and end users;
  - phytotoxic effects.

Chemical parameters to be measured are specified and with respect to landfill gas, emissions of CH_4 and CO_2 are to be monitored for at least 12 months.

Annex II of the note gives further brief guidance on assessment techniques for gas-emitting sites.

4.2.6 Waste Management Paper No. 27, *Landfill Gas* (2nd Edition – 1991)

WMP27 is intended to provide guidance on the monitoring and control of landfill gas and is probably the most quoted (and misquoted) source of guidance on the assessment of landfill gas hazards.

The document concentrates mainly upon the specific techniques which may be employed to monitor and control landfill gas (principally at source) and gives relatively little specific guidance on appropriate site investigation strategies. The guidance that is given is summarised below.

1. A desk study should be undertaken to include geology, hydrogeology, topography, land use and development, other gas sources and disposal/site characteristics and history.

2. A preliminary physical appraisal should be undertaken to confirm and add information to that obtained during the desk study.

3. Surface monitoring for flammable gas should be undertaken on and around the site, followed by subsurface monitoring within buried services or by probes. If no gas is found it cannot be concluded that none is being evolved.

4. The assessment may be concluded at this stage if no development is proposed or at risk from the site and there is no evidence of gas generation or likely evolution.

5. Where development (existing and proposed) is on or adjacent to a landfill, or the desk study indicates that the landfill is likely to produce large volumes of gas, then a geological and hydrogeological investigation of the site and its surroundings should be undertaken (in accordance with paragraphs 3.109 and 3.119 of Waste Management Paper No. 26) to a distance of at least 250 m from the site boundary, and beyond if there are migration pathways allowing migration beyond this limit.

6. Where development is within 250 m of the landfill a survey should be undertaken of the landfill and the area between the landfill and the development.

7. A survey is unlikely to be adequate unless boreholes and wells are drilled both within and outside the wastes (for hydrological and hydrogeological data and waste characteristics).

8. An adequate number of boreholes should be drilled to provide assurance that a representative proportion of migration pathways are monitored.

9. Specialist advice should be sought on borehole spacings, sampling frequency and interpretation of results.

10. Where development is proposed and no information on landfill gas evolution is available, an investigation should be undertaken in accordance with DoE Circular 21/87, and specialist advice should be sought to assess the gas risk if gas is found.

11. A pattern of gas concentrations in and around the site should be established over a period of time and in different weather conditions.

12. The baseline for detection of migrating gases from a site will need to be varied where methane and carbon dioxide from other external sources are found in high concentrations.

13. There may be a wide range of background concentrations of carbon dioxide in the ground around sites.

14. Where it is thought that the gas sampled is not landfill gas, but the site is near to a landfill site, then an investigation should be undertaken to determine the background concentration in the locality.

Waste Management Paper No. 27 gives detailed advice for the monitoring of landfill gas and indicative criteria for gas risk with respect to gas levels in relation to monitoring on a gas-generating site, i.e. landfill, from the point of view of a site operator or owner rather than a developer or owner of an adjacent potentially affected site. The principal points to be noted are:

1. A monitoring programme should include the provision of monitoring points beyond the site boundary and particularly between the landfill and any development.

2. When regular monitoring shows conditions at a site are regular and a predictable pattern occurs then the monitoring frequency may be reduced, but to not less than six-monthly intervals.

3. Monitoring should continue until:

    a. the maximum concentration of flammable gas from biodegradation within the landfill remains less than 1% by volume (20% LEL) and the concentration of carbon dioxide from biodegradation within the landfill remains less than 1.5%

by volume measured in any monitoring point within the wastes over a 24 month period taken on at least four separate occasions, including two occasions when atmospheric pressure was falling and was below 1000 mb; or

b.   an examination of the waste using an appropriate statistical sampling method provides a 95% level of confidence that the biodegradable matter in the waste has been used up.

4.   At landfill sites where analyses of core material recovered from the waste show that none of the waste is biodegradable, but low concentrations of landfill gas are found, monitoring may be ceased (if acceptable to the planning or waste regulation authorities).

5.   Monitoring using wells and boreholes is the preferred method.

6.   At completed and shallow landfill sites adequate short-term monitoring may be achieved using excavated pits or trenches.

7.   At every landfill site where there is potential for gas to migrate to development or underground services, monitoring boreholes should be installed at appropriate points outside the wastes and between the landfill and any development potentially at risk.

8.   Monitoring from trial pits should take place over a number of weeks because air will be introduced into the ground during construction.

9.   Monitoring wells within the waste should not penetrate the base of the waste but boreholes outside the waste should go to a depth below the waste deposits depending upon the geology and hydrogeology.

10.   Sufficient time should be allowed for the system to equilibrate after borehole installation (typically two or three weeks).

11.   Borehole location and spacing are site specific. The optimum pattern, design and distribution of gas monitoring boreholes and wells should be determined by specialist advice.

12.   Typical borehole spacings will generally range from 50 m upwards for uniform strata with no development within 250 m, to between 5 and 20 m near development on fissured strata and adjoining a landfill site. This is general guidance and will vary with geology, waste generation characteristics and development proximity.

Specifically in relation to development on or around landfill sites WMP27 states:

(a)   DoE Circulars 21/87 and 17/89 outline the measures needed to conduct a survey of a completed landfill to assess its suitability for development. ICRCL Guidance Note 17/78 *Notes on the Development and After-use of Landfill Sites* and approved building Codes of Practice should also be consulted

(b)   Domestic housing should not be built on landfills which are gassing or have the potential to produce significant quantities of gas

(c)   Where housing development is proposed no house, shed, greenhouse or extension should be constructed within 50 m of the infilled wastes and no garden should extend to within 10 m of the wastes, where the landfill is actively producing or has the potential to produce large quantities of gas.

4.2.7   BRE, *Construction of New Buildings on Gas-contaminated Land* (1991)

This document was produced to supplement the revision of Approved Document C of the Building Regulations (see below) which refers specifically to landfill gas risk to new structures. In the light of this the publication refers predominantly to gas control and exclusion measures in buildings and gives no specific recommendations for the investigation of sites at potential risk from methane. It does, however, acknowledge three important difficulties in setting trigger levels for methane risk:

1. Gas concentration can vary significantly with time.

2. The risk relates to methane's explosive properties which are difficult to quantify in comparison to, for instance, the health effects of toxic substances.

3. Background concentrations of methane and carbon dioxide are seldom zero and often variable.

4.2.8 The Building Regulations Approved Document C (1992)

The document gives specific guidance on measures to be incorporated into developments to resist moisture. Insofar as the document gives guidance on site preparation, general guidance is given on the problems associated with the presence of contaminants including landfill gas. This guidance is as follows:

1. Where there is a potential for gas risk to a building further investigation should be made to determine what, if any, protective measures are necessary.

2. Where the level of methane in the ground is unlikely to exceed 1% by volume no further protection needs to be provided if the ground floor of the building is of suspended concrete construction and ventilated.

3. Carbon dioxide concentrations should be considered independently of methane levels. Concentrations exceeding 1.5% by volume in the ground indicate a need to consider gas exclusion measures. A level of 5% implies that specific design measures are required.

4. Active mechanical ventilation is not usually feasible. Passive protection is generally the only viable alternative where gas concentration in the ground is low.

5. For non-domestic buildings expert advice should be sought as to the level and need for a gas investigation.

6. The amount of gas in the ground and its pressure relative to atmosphere should be measured as well as concentration. High gas concentrations have less impact if the gas volume is small, for example from limited deposits of peat, silt, etc.

7. The investigation results and expert advice should be used to assess the present and future gas risk with extended monitoring if necessary.

4.2.9 Other published guidance

The guidance summarised in Sections 4.2.1 to 4.2.8 inclusive can be considered as official guidance in that it was all issued by central government, i.e. the Department of the Environment or its executive agencies. There is, however, other equally credible guidance issued by non-governmental organisations. The main documents quoted are the BSI publication DD175 *Code of Practice for the Identification of Potentially Contaminated Land and its Investigation*, the Institute of Wastes Management document *Monitoring of Landfill Gas* and the BS 5930 *Code of Practice for Site Investigations*. These are discussed briefly below.

BS 5930: 1981

Although there is no specific guidance in this document relating to methane, very detailed guidance is given on the investigation of sites for assessing their suitability for construction projects. The issues discussed are dealt with in considerable detail and while now apparently dated, BS 5930 still forms the basis of good investigation practice.

DD175: 1988

This publication gives detailed guidelines on the factors which may be pertinent to an investigation of a contaminated site and indicates the logistical implications of structuring an investigation. While the guidelines are comprehensive they do not provide specific guidance on the investigation and assessment of gas risk to development in any detail.

Institute of Wastes Management – *Monitoring of Landfill Gas* **(1989)**

This guidance document provides detailed information on all aspects of gas generation and monitoring under a variety of conditions. Case studies are presented to illustrate the problems associated with monitoring landfill gas. Some of the relevant comments made in the document are:

- all sites should be monitored on at least four occasions over two years

- for active sites the installation of monitoring boreholes will be required

- if quantitative data on gas generation are required then boreholes are necessary. Gas quantity, pressure and temperature may also be assessed using trial pits

- monitoring strategies will differ between completed, operational and proposed landfill sites

- the maximum distance between boreholes under any circumstances should be 50 m (under review).

The document also provides useful information on the appropriateness of specific monitoring techniques and methods for distinguishing landfill gas from other sources of gas.

4.2.10   Literature review – discussion and summary

It is clear from the above summaries that there is no shortage of guidance available and there is a some degree of commonality between the different guidance documents. The ease with which this guidance can be applied to specific investigation or development scenarios, however, is questionable in the light of some of the significant shortcomings of these publications, principally:

1. All the guidance is of a general nature and not easily identifiable with a particular investigation scenario or development context.

2. The guidance concentrates mainly on landfill gas and, in particular, the investigation and monitoring of landfill sites themselves rather than adjacent sites. Very little mention is made of gas sources other than landfill and their likely hazards.

3. Although there appears to be some degree of consistency across the documents with respect to the general principles involved, there are some significant inconsistencies, mainly in relation to adequate monitoring periods and the appropriateness of certain techniques.

4. There is frequent referral to other guidance documents for more detailed guidance on particular issues, but, the guidance is very general.

5. The generality of the guidance often leads to a degree of ambiguity in some documents, particularly Waste Management Paper No. 27. For example, it is asserted that if subsurface sampling does not identify gas it cannot be taken as certain that none is present, and then goes on to state that the investigation may be concluded at this stage, albeit in certain circumstances, where there is no evidence of gas generation.

6. Attempts are made to introduce some kind of uniformity to investigations which may lead to excessive or unwarranted measures. For example, the criterion of a minimum 250-m wide zone of risk around landfill sites takes no account of the gas generation and migration potential of individual sites. Thus, the same 250-m criterion would be ascribed to a large domestic landfill in permeable strata and to a small 'inert' site in low permeability strata. While the zone may be increased for greater risk sites (e.g. the former case) there is no allowance for its reduction (the latter case).

   Similarly, spacing criteria are set for sampling points based on a uniform grid pattern, which although efficient may not be representative.

   There is a contradiction in logic between the unanimous assertion that each case is (and should be considered as) site specific and recommendations of adherence to absolute criteria. (A preferable approach would be the presentation of indicative criteria with the recommendation that specific values should be chosen on the basis of judgement).

7. None of the documents gives guidance on how to assess the results in the context of the objectives for which they were obtained.

Notwithstanding the above comments there is also a great deal of essential guidance applicable to any investigation strategy, i.e.

- Every case is unique and thus each site investigation should specific to that site.
- A comprehensive desk study should be undertaken at the outset and developed throughout the investigation as necessary.
- The investigation should be a staged and iterative process building upon and confirming the results of the preceding stages.
- There is a strong need for expert involvement in obtaining and assessing the results of an investigation.

Providing these documents are used for guidance and not taken to be a rigid specification, then they are important reference sources and a starting point for any investigation.

4.3 GOOD CURRENT PRACTICE

There is generally a high degree of consistency among experienced practitioners (from the public and private sectors) with regard to the general principles of site investigation and the procedural stages an investigation would normally be expected to go through. This generally comprises the following steps:

Step 1 : Desk study and site visit

(possibly incorporating a spiking survey).

Step 2 : Preliminary site investigation

Principally a data gathering exercise intended to define the physical and environmental context of the site and establish an initial gas monitoring dataset indicative of the gas regime and its potential hazard.

Step 3 : Detailed site investigation

A comprehensive and thorough investigation of the site, using data from the previous steps to design an effective monitoring programme incorporating a sufficient number, and distribution, of appropriate monitoring installations, to give as scientifically sound and as representative a set of data relating to the gas regime as is practicable. This should enable a confident assessment to be made of the risk presented by the gas for a specific scenario and the measures necessary to mitigate that risk effectively.

Although, in general, the above steps should apply to all site investigations the specific objectives and component actions of each step should be site specific and determined by factors such as those outlined in Section 2. That is not to say that in many cases the same strategy may not be applied to different development scenarios.

The vast majority of gas-specific site investigations relate to landfill as the principal source; in comparison there is little experience of gas investigations for mine gas and hardly any experience of site investigations where natural peat or silt deposits constitute the likely methane hazard to development. Consequently much of the discussion that follows is in the context of methane and carbon dioxide hazards to development on or adjacent to landfill sites. The principles are nevertheless relevant to the other potential gas sources. The various stages of a typical investigation are discussed below.

4.3.1 The desk study

All the parties consulted agreed that every investigation must start with a desk study which should include as much information as possible about the site and its surroundings from whatever sources are considered appropriate. Even where gas is discovered during an on-going ground investigation it will be necessary to attempt to identify the likely gas source and its potential occurrence before further gas-specific investigation can be commenced.

The main objectives of the desk study should be to identify and locate, or at least indicate, the likely generation potential of the suspected gas source and to identify all the characteristics of the site and its environs, especially the geology and hydrogeology, that may influence or affect the risk posed by the gas to the potential receptors. This should include an initial assessment of potential gas sources other than those which appear most obvious.

While these objectives were generally agreed by the consultees there was some variation in their view of how these objectives should be achieved. The majority of consultees considered that the starting point of the investigation should be an appraisal of maps, plans and aerial photographs of the site and area (including geological maps), accompanied by more site specific data relating to the site history and use, from available records and reports.

The areas of disagreement amongst practitioners primarily related to (1) the method of gathering the data, (2) need for an accompanying site visit and (3) the use of anecdotal evidence. It was considered by some practitioners that all records and historical data such as planning registers, site licences, etc. should be inspected in person at the office in which they are held. This is because of the fact that, as confirmed by a few local authorities, the officers retrieving the data for a written or telephoned request have to apply their own discretion or interpretation as to what the investigator needs to know and, given their time and work constraints may miss, or not impart, potentially useful or even essential information.

Most practitioners stated that a site visit ought to accompany a desk study regardless of the currency or detail of the records obtained. This was considered necessary to verify the information from the desk study with respect to the physical layout of the site and surroundings and also to highlight other significant factors that may not have been recorded. While all parties agreed this was necessary, some believed that it must be done prior to any physical or intrusive survey, whereas some considered that it could be done during the preliminary investigation. In general, however, it is preferred if a site visit and walkover precede any physical investigation.

The greatest area of disagreement amongst practitioners concerned the credibility of anecdotal evidence from local residents, etc. Views ranged from total disregard of anecdotal evidence, as being invariably inaccurate and usually highly misleading, to consistent inclusion of anecdotal sources in the desk study where available. As an example of the former case, an unnecessary and fruitless investigation was undertaken where tipping on a site had been claimed by a local resident and none was actually found. In the latter case, a large gassing waste mass was identified on a supposedly greenfield development site following comments by a local resident. The general consensus of opinion from practitioners was that anecdotal evidence was potentially of value if treated with caution and used only to corroborate existing information or highlight specific areas of a site that might warrant further investigation.

Some specific comments of relevance made by individual consultees with respect to the desk study are:

1. Not enough information has been gathered for a desk study until it can be confidently defended as complete in a court of law (i.e. the most rigorous test of its adequacy).

2. The quality of response to information requests varies considerably amongst the local authorities.

3. The originally proposed 'registers of land subject to contaminative uses' (compiled under section 143 of the Environmental Protection Act 1990) would be an extremely useful and efficient source of information for desk studies of this nature.

4. All information obtained should be confirmed in writing to substantiate the need for further detailed investigation, where appropriate.

4.3.2 Walk-over survey

This should put the physical characteristics of the site into the context of the desk study and allow confirmation of the surface features identified in the desk study with the actual situation. It should also be used to identify potential problem areas such as likely migration pathways, vegetation die-back, recent or unrecorded sensitive receptors such as buildings, services, crops, etc. Notes should be made of any physical changes in the site compared with the desk study records.

The walk-over survey could also include a spiking survey, but this is typically incorporated into the early stages of the preliminary assessment which is discussed below.

4.3.3 Preliminary investigation

The preliminary investigation should, first, confirm the presence of gas in the study area and, secondly, provide a short-term, semi-quantitative database upon which, in conjunction with the desk study information, the detailed investigation should be designed.

This stage of the investigation should typically involve the use of shallow techniques such as spiking, driven probes and trial pits. However, boreholes may also be installed at this stage where it is obvious or likely from the desk study that they will be needed (e.g. if deep-seated migration is suspected).

4.3.4 Detailed site investigation

In most cases a detailed site investigation should follow a preliminary investigation, although there have been circumstances where a detailed investigation has followed directly from a desk study. In general, however, the results of the preliminary investigation should have highlighted specific areas for special attention such as zones of high gas activity or potential migration pathways.

In most cases the detailed investigation would necessitate the installation of boreholes, mainly because they provide a long-term robust installation capable of intercepting potential gas pockets or susceptible geology at depth. Where the nature of the proposed, or at-risk, development is such that long-term or deep monitoring is not necessary it is likely that only a few or even no boreholes will be necessary. Instead an expansion in number and distribution of the trial pits and standpipes may suffice, e.g. where informal open space or soft landscaping is proposed on the site.

4.3.5 Supplementary investigation

The use of other techniques such a flux boxes or incubation tests may also be employed but only as a supplementary data gathering exercise within the broad procedural stages outlined above. It is also possible that the detailed investigation may indicate specific areas where further investigation is warranted. For example, if a zone of gas migration is identified further installations may be needed to determine the extent of migration in that particular area.

4.4 TECHNIQUES

Practitioners also commented on the use and appropriateness of common techniques.

4.4.1 Spiking

There appears to be a considerable divergence in attitude towards spiking and its adequacy as an investigation technique. All consultees agreed that the effectiveness of spiking is limited to near-surface effects; and on this basis many interviewees did not recommend its use, because the information obtained was so unrepresentative of the general gas regime that it was useless or misleading. Furthermore, a spiking survey can do no more than confirm the likely presence of gas near the surface, and whatever the result (negative or positive) it does not alter the need for further investigation. Thus, on the whole, it can be a redundant step.

Despite the apparent lack of confidence in this technique, its use is still advocated by some parties as an initial assessment method and many local authorities prioritised the risk potential of closed landfill sites in their area on the basis of spike surveys. This must clearly be an interim measure as a spike survey, no matter how extensive, cannot reliably indicate the overall gas regime within the ground mass. Some planning authorities are prepared to accept a site investigation report for small developments (e.g. extensions or conservatories) on the basis of a one-off spiking survey, where a gas survey is required to comply with the General Development Order. This is not considered by most consultees to be good practice.

Notwithstanding this, the technique is still used occasionally where additional data are required on surface emissions, e.g. to confirm that gas is present in the root zone where die-back has been observed. The main conclusion to be drawn about the use of spiking is that it should only be used to provide supporting data, e.g. to confirm the presence of gas where it was already suspected near the surface. The results should not be used as the sole basis for decisions or actions.

4.4.2   Trial pits

Backfilled trial pits with a gas probe are a widely used technique and considered to be appropriate to most site investigations. The majority of practitioners state that under certain circumstances a trial pit investigation should be sufficient to obtain adequate gas monitoring data to make an assessment of the risk to a proposed development, typically where the development site is adjacent to a raised landfill, or a shallow site that is of a similar depth to a trial pit (up to 5 m). In general, however, they are considered as a short-term, shallow technique to accompany or precede a borehole investigation, acting both as gas monitoring installations and, equally importantly, as a method of inspecting the physical state of the waste and likely extent of degradation (*via* visual and laboratory examination).

Under certain circumstances trial pits would not be as appropriate for a preliminary site investigation as a borehole. For example where a site is a deep landfill or the proposed development is an underground structure such as a tunnel, then the information obtained from the near-surface monitoring allowed by a trial pit is likely to be less representative than that obtained from boreholes. There are further limitations with installing trial pits with respect to the extensive ground disturbance caused and access needed for the plant; this for, example, is likely to preclude the use of trial pits in residential or built-up areas.

4.4.3   Driven probes

Driven probes should be employed as a supplementary or intermediate technique to boreholes and trial pits. The depth to which they can be driven is generally greater than for trial pits. They also allow the opportunity to measure water levels and, as such, provide a useful extra source of data for the preliminary investigation.

4.4.4   Boreholes

Boreholes are probably the most widely employed technique for site investigations for methane and it is likely that they will be necessary for most investigations, especially during the detailed stage of investigation. It is not uncommon, however, for a number of boreholes to be drilled as part of the preliminary investigation, to determine, for example, water levels, or to confirm the geological sequence in potential migration pathways or gas source strata, near to sensitive receptors such as buildings or services. Notwithstanding the specific gas issues, boreholes are usually incorporated into a pre-development ground investigation anyway.

In general, boreholes should be installed to the depth of the likely source for subterranean gas sources such as mine gas and some buried peat or silt deposits. For landfill gas, most practitioners consider that boreholes adjacent to landfill sites should be drilled to the full depth of the deposited waste and/or intercepting permeable geology or groundwater. It is typically asserted, however, that boreholes should not be taken to the full depth of wastes when installed on a landfill as they may breach any basal containment that exists and can alter or re-activate the gas generation characteristics of the site. Care should thus be taken when deciding to install boreholes in a landfill.

4.5 MONITORING STRATEGY

4.5.1 Monitoring period

Among most practitioners it was considered that in order for the dataset obtained from the monitoring installations to be representative, and thus allow confident assessment of the gas regime, monitoring should take place for a minimum of three months, providing that within those three months there was a variation in influencing conditions such as barometric pressure and the physical condition of the ground surface. In general, the longer the period of monitoring the better.

4.5.2 Monitoring frequency

The general frequency for monitoring would typically be weekly for several weeks which could be extended to fortnightly, then monthly intervals, depending upon the consistency of the results. The more variable the results from one monitoring occasion to the next, then the more frequent the monitoring should be.

The number of occasions on which monitoring should take place should be related to the consistency of the gas regime in terms of gas concentration and composition. As a general rule monitoring should take place more frequently if there is no clear trend or reproducibility in the results: this obviously requires a larger dataset to enable the identification of trends or a baseline. Where the results are consistent from one week to the next then the monitoring frequency may be reduced. As a general guide a minimum of approximately 6-10 monitoring visits should suffice where the latter case applies, although the opportunity to monitor during worst case conditions, such as rapidly falling barometric pressure or following recent heavy rain, should be taken wherever possible rather than rigidly adhering to a formalised regular timetable.

4.5.3 Distribution of monitoring points

When deciding where to locate the monitoring installations for the detailed investigation, it was felt that the following areas should be considered as the prime target locations:

1. Areas of high gas activity or 'hot spots'.
2. Critical areas between the gas source and the development site (existing or proposed) if they are close to or adjacent to each other. For example, where a development site is close to a landfill the critical area would be at the development site boundary nearest the landfill, especially in areas with increased migration potential (permeable geology, service runs, roads, etc.). The depth at which the potential migration pathways lie should influence the choice of installation (e.g. trial pits for surface pathways, boreholes for deep ones). This would obviously not apply where the gas source was deeper subterranean gas such as mine gas or deep natural gas reservoirs.
3. Areas of proposed development sites that would be more sensitive to gas risk, e.g. buildings, manholes, service runs and any areas of the site that may provide collection voids or cavities in or above the ground.

4. Between the development site and other sensitive development where off-site migration may be promoted. For example, where surface emission is occurring on the development site, subsequent surface sealing by 'hard cover' may force the gas to migrate laterally to adjacent sites. It would be prudent, therefore, to employ monitoring installations at the site perimeter where sensitive receptors on the adjacent site, such as housing, lie beyond.

The list of target areas described above is not considered to be exhaustive and such an approach could be devised for numerous site specific circumstances. Generally, the above target scenarios should be considered as likely starting points for more detailed investigation.

In addition to all the specific areas requiring special attention, the detailed investigation should extend to the rest of the site not already covered in the above scenarios. In these areas it is acceptable to use a grid approach depending upon the nature and extent of monitoring undertaken in the preliminary investigation.

For instance, if a grid pattern of trial pits in these areas yielded no significant gas results, deeper installations such as boreholes or driven probes may be used adjacent to, or spaced between, the trial pits to assess the deeper regime. Depending upon the sensitivity of these areas with respect to the proposed end-use of the site, the trial pits may suffice and no further investigation may be warranted in this area.

The investigation strategy should always be an iterative approach, responding to the previous stages of the investigation. As an example in the case above, the deeper installations may indicate significant gas activity at depth, not identified by the trial pits, thus the detailed investigation may identify other areas or locations of special interest for further investigation.

4.5.4   Number of monitoring points

The number and distribution of monitoring installations to be used is site specific and depends, amongst other things, upon the particular techniques to be employed and the results of the previous stages of the investigation. It is generally considered that a regular grid-pattern of monitoring points is appropriate only to the preliminary investigation for establishing ground conditions and the general 'baseline' gas and water regime, and possibly for highlighting areas of higher or more significant gas emission.

A minimum number of monitoring installations is difficult to define, but the aim should be to gain enough information to give confidence that the likely variations in the gas regime and influencing conditions had been encountered. For the preliminary assessment it may be acceptable to have indicative spacing criteria for certain investigation scenarios on the basis that a grid pattern would be adequate at this stage. Thus the closeness of the spacing would reflect the predicted magnitude and significance of the gas hazard. Consequently, the number of monitoring points to be installed will be determined mainly by the size of the area under investigation and the appropriate spacing.

The number of monitoring points needed for the detailed investigation should reflect, first, the size and nature of the areas requiring detailed investigation and, secondly, the perceived gas hazard to those areas. Thus for a particularly sensitive area (e.g. proposed building plot) with a low perceived gas hazard (from the preliminary assessment), more monitoring points should be used than for a less sensitive or higher gas activity area. This is because the effort required to prove gas is present is usually less than the effort required to prove gas is not present. The number required would depend upon what is perceived as a model of the gas regime in the ground and achieving a coverage anticipated as necessary to confirm the model and make confident decisions. This has to be specific to the individual location of each monitoring point and to the local ground and groundwater conditions and the site geology.

4.5.5 Monitoring parameters

The parameters to be monitored, as a minimum, should comprise the gas composition with respect to methane, carbon dioxide and oxygen and the concentration of each of these gases as a percentage. Of comparable importance is the rate of emission, as this determines how much gas could be presented to the receptors in question[3]. The barometric pressure and ground conditions (e.g. wet, frozen, snow covered, desiccated) should also be recorded. The barometric pressure in itself is less critical than the rate of change prior to monitoring, as it is the differential pressure between the gas in the ground and atmosphere that provides the pressure gradient to promote or inhibit the emission of gas. The pressure at the time of monitoring may be in equilibrium with the gas regime and therefore of little influence.

On this latter point the practitioners considered the guidance in Waste Management Paper No. 27 to be misleading. It requires that the pressure on two occasions should be falling and below 1000 mb, thus implying that this is a worst case condition. In fact, the worst case, in terms of influencing gas emission, is likely to be when there is a rapid rate of fall in barometric pressure, whether this fall takes place over a high range or a low range.

In general, most practitioners considered that measurements with field instruments are satisfactory for assessing the gas regime, providing that they are properly calibrated and certified. Regular confirmation by gas chromatography as a calibration check *per se*, is not considered necessary. However, gas chromatography or infra-red analysis should be used to confirm significant results where the accuracy is important (e.g. if the results are to be used for a significant decision such as choice of end-use, or litigation where a high level of confidence is needed in the results or where anomalous readings are apparent). The main use of gas chromatography will be in the indication of the possible gas source where its origin is not clear or compounded by two or more potential sources (see References 2 and 3).

The generalised strategy above has been developed from extensive experience in a wide variety of investigation contexts and can be considered as a summarised account of good practice as developed by competent practitioners in the UK. There must obviously be a rationale or set of influencing criteria in order to establish such a strategy. These influencing factors and reasons for some of the assertions made are discussed below.

4.6 FACTORS INFLUENCING AN INVESTIGATION STRATEGY

The factors which may have an influence on the investigation strategy are:
1. Purpose of the investigation.
2. Nature of the gas source/risk.
3. Type of development/potential receptor.
4. Location of the development/receptor site.
5. Existing level of knowledge.
6. Logistical and cost implications.

In ideal terms, purpose may be considered to be common to all investigations, namely to measure and assess the hazard due to methane in the ground and to determine appropriate control measures. The overall strategy should be directed towards fulfilling this purpose regardless of the specific occasion for the investigation. Thus, the nature of the data to be obtained should be unaffected by, for example, considerations of whether the information is to be used for a planning application or an assessment of an existing development. Similarly, while cost, time and logistical considerations have to be taken into account, the value of the investigation can be jeopardised if they become overriding factors. In reality it is inevitable that such factors will influence the strategy, but care should be exercised to maintain a proper balance and to ensure that external constraints do not unduly inhibit the execution of an adequate investigation.

The nature of the gas source is influential in that the site investigation strategy should reflect the way in which the gas hazard presents itself, which may vary according to the source. The following example scenarios illustrate this:

(a) Where the source is from an adjacent landfill which is relatively deep, an effective strategy would be to install a line of boreholes between the development site and landfill to 'intercept' any migrating gas close to the landfill. They will also need to extend to the full depth of the waste and/or groundwater or susceptible strata

(b) Where the situation is similar to that of (a), but the landfill site is shallow (say less than 5 m), the same strategy may be applied but employing trial pits or driven probes, instead of boreholes.

(c) If the likely gas source is from coal measures or workings beneath the development site, the above strategy would be inappropriate as there is no zone of interception in any particular part of the site. The whole site would have to be investigated by means of boreholes, probably to the depth of the suspected gas-bearing strata or workings.

The type of development or receptor is influential in some respects in that it is generally accepted that the level of investigation and rigour with which the investigation should be carried out can be less for a 'soft' end-use (e.g. informal open space) than a 'hard' end-use (e.g. buildings).

It is not considered acceptable, however, to lessen the degree of risk definition for controllable, low occupancy or managed development such as warehouses or commercial units compared to freehold housing. The opposite view is taken by some parties on the basis that management and maintenance of the gas control measures is practical in the former case, but not in the latter. Most practitioners considered that it would still be necessary to assess the risk thoroughly in order to design adequate control measures.

In general, however, the investigation strategy should be determined largely by the way in which the gas hazard is manifested rather than by the potential hazard receptors. As such the only major distinction drawn is between hard and soft end-uses.

The location of the development site is obviously important in terms of its proximity to the gas source. Thus, the investigation strategy for a development site near a landfill would not necessarily be the same as for a development site on a former landfill.

The existing level of knowledge about the risk to the development site from gas will affect the amount and type of information that a site investigation must impart to make a competent risk assessment. This should be reflected in the strategy *via* the type, number and location of monitoring points required.

On the whole it can be seen that there is a general approach towards site investigation for methane which can be considered to be current good practice. The identified protocols and procedures are developed into a comprehensive set of guidelines in Sections 5 and 6. It is also important, however, to consider the requirements and perceptions of other parties that may be involved in the investigation of methane risk sites, principally the local authorities, developers, insurers and funders.

4.7   LOCAL AUTHORITY PERSPECTIVE

It was known at the start of this research project, and reconfirmed during it, that practitioners and local authorities often take different views on what constitutes an adequate methane investigation – either in general terms or specifically for a particular site. It is worthwhile examining when and why these differences arise.

First, the various responsibilities on local authorities mean that different departments have different standpoints, although all have the overriding concern for public safety. Second, their involvement with a site, where methane might be or is a hazard, comes at different stages of the site's development.

In general, the waste regulation authorities take an approach to methane investigation which is incorporated into Sections 4.3, 4.4 and 4.5, along with the views of experienced specialists. Where there are divergences from that broad approach these tend to be at the planning application stage. Developers and their professional advisers have commented that there are times when local authority requirements are more onerous and less flexible than they consider necessary.

By way of examples, the following statements illustrate the types of investigation requirements that have been set by some local authorities:

- 'For a site investigation to be adequate, boreholes must be installed; trial pits and driven probes can only provide supplementary data'

- 'Monitoring should preferably take place for 2 years to provide an adequate data set and at least 1 or 2 measurements should be made when the barometric pressure is below 1000 mb. A minimum of 6 months monitoring must be done'

- 'Boreholes must be installed on an X m grid pattern and taken to Y m below the wastes'

- 'A minimum number of Z boreholes must be installed per site'

- 'There must be gas chromatographic confirmation of a number of results (e.g. 10%) for each monitoring visit'.

Many local authorities take the pragmatic view that investigations should be designed to suit the specific site circumstances, and all recognise that the thoroughness or adequacy of an investigation is not determined by setting, say, minimum numbers of boreholes. Nevertheless, blanket requirements, such as those above, are imposed: often their effect is counterproductive for the following reasons:

1. Compliance with a prescribed formula for an investigation could lead to either unnecessary cost or, more importantly, absorbing costs which would better be spent on a more focused investigation.

2. The risks of protracted delays at the planning stage or before development can start or, even, of refusal of an application could lead to overcautious provisions in the design of gas control measures for the development. In the extreme these additional costs, whether of delay or construction, could affect the economic viability of the proposed development.

On the other hand, the local authorities follow the 'official' guidance described earlier (Section 4.2) or apply it as best they can to their circumstances and in the light of their experience.

If they attempt to follow the official guidance, however complete or appropriate it is, the local authorities are criticised if they are thought to misapply or misinterpret it. If they do not follow it, they are or could be criticised, unfair as it may be, by appearing to ignore it. This puts a difficult burden on public servants who do not necessarily have the specialist knowledge to judge when technical guidelines are appropriate and when not.

An example of this difficulty concerns the 1.5% carbon dioxide threshold relating to landfill sites (Waste Management Paper No: 27). Higher proportions of carbon dioxide can be measured on non-waste sites as normal background concentrations, but without being considered as presenting a significant hazard. The point is that the 1.5% CO_2 threshold is not, in itself, relevant to these other sites, however great the temptation to apply it in the absence of other, relevant guidelines.

Four other factors are likely to influence the local authority perspective:

1. Their body of experience and knowledge.
2. A desire for uniformity or similarity of standards in a subject influenced by many variables.
3. Experience of variable quality of investigations, their methods and reports and, consequently, potentially inadequate planning applications and expensive inquiries.
4. Insufficient consultation and cooperation from developers or their professional advisers during the design and implementation stages of the investigation.

This last factor is particularly important. If local authorities perceive developers as commissioning minimum investigations apparently sufficient only to gain planning permission, they will impose their requirements.

Specialists, on the other hand, have an obligation to minimise investigation to achieve the optimal results of necessary information at least cost and as quickly as possible. As such if they are able to explain and justify their proposals to the local authority, as they do to their client, there is more likely to be positive interaction between them. The key stage is the desk study report which presents the initial assessment of a potential gas hazard and should set out the scheme of physical investigation, and the philosophy underlying it.

Rather than setting quantity requirements for the investigations and checking that these have been executed, it is preferable to stipulate, first, that there is thorough desk study reported with a plan for the preliminary and detailed investigation (accepting that this should be flexible depending upon what is found and on how the development's siting might be modified); and, second, that there should be evidence of adherence to the plan or justification for changes from it.

This would call for greater interaction between developers, their advisers and the local authorities, but it could be of benefit in several ways:

- avoidance of unnecessary investigation
- improved, more focused, investigation
- fewer protracted discussions at the planning application stage or expensive inquiries and appeals
- shortening of the time, in some cases, before construction starts

- fewer cases of over-cautious design of gas control measures, i.e. lower construction costs.

Case study 2 (Section 4.9.2) is an example which highlights the last point. The developers chose the option presented of monitoring the site for six months and installing comprehensive control measures rather than monitoring for two years to define the gas risk.

4.8   OTHER INTERESTED PARTIES

In addition to the practitioners and competent authorities there are typically three other interested groups with respect to the adequacy of the site investigation: developers, funders and insurers.

4.8.1   Developers

Developers, although the main protagonists in the development, rarely carry out the site investigation themselves. This task, including the design and implementation of an adequate investigation strategy, is usually charged to their consultants, the practitioners.

Both commercial and residential developers were consulted during this research. Their perception of the problems and adequacy of investigation for methane-risk sites raises a number of issues.

The main comments made by some of the housing developers (either directly from interview or *via* the practitioners/authorities) can be summarised as follows:

1. Often there is no attempt to look for problems such as gases or contamination during the initial site appraisal (unless its presence is obvious). This is because of the prospective developer's conventional interest primarily in the geotechnical stability of the ground, and often the time constraints imposed by a competitive tendering situation do not allow more detailed assessment at the pre-acquisition/ development design stage.

2. If either the initial appraisal or the local authority indicates that gas may be a problem, the developer will often commission a specific gas investigation or incorporate one into the specification of the general engineering site investigation (assuming the development proposals are now decided upon).

3. In areas where potential problems with gas are common (as for example in certain areas of the West Midlands where high carbon dioxide levels are typical), the developer may make provision in the initial costing for gas exclusion measures in the properties (this may typically add around 10% to the plot costs of a typical starter home), but may lose out on winning tenders as a result.

4. It is now generally considered good practice to consult the local authority at an early stage and maintain contact throughout the investigation and application processes.

5. Some of the main problems, as seen by a housing developer in relation to the local authorities and planning process are:

    (a) Planners usually delegate assessment of the technical issues, such as gas, to the Environmental Health Department which frequently has neither the resources nor expertise to appraise the investigation and assessment; consequently they adhere to a strict interpretation of guidelines such as Waste Management Paper No. 27.

(b) Although the National House-Building Council staff generally understand the issues, planners and environmental health officers often do not; thus protracted conflicts arise amongst the various authorising parties.

(c) Undue reliance by some authorities on specific aspects of guidance which may be inappropriate to a particular development may lead to over-specification of the site investigation and exclusion measures required.

(d) Sales are sometimes lost through panic or over-reaction by building surveyors or solicitors on discovering from local authority searches that the property is on a site recorded as having a potential gas risk, even though this risk has been mitigated to the satisfaction of the authority.

6. Generally, most queries made to developers in relation to the sale of properties on potential gas-risk sites address the adequacy of the specific gas-control or exclusion measures and not the risk assessment and site investigation, although a buildings insurance company has requested copies of the site investigation reports prior to deciding on whether or not to cover a property.

Commercial developments such as light industrial units, offices and superstores are becoming more common on or adjacent to contaminated land, including landfill sites. This marginal land is attractive to many commercial developers because it is invariably cheaper to acquire than greenfield sites. The acquisition of such sites, however, is considered to be a balancing act because the cost of investigating the site for gas, and implementing acceptable control measures, may result in the ultimate development costs exceeding those of a greenfield site, where such measures would not be necessary.

A major superstore chain with considerable experience of development on landfill sites commented on a number of issues relating to the development of such sites. The first site they developed, interestingly, was investigated for gas because the developer and local fire authority were concerned about the potential risk to the occupants of the store from methane. While this in itself is not unusual, the initiation of the gas investigation pre-dated the Loscoe explosion, the incident that triggered the current concern over methane risks to development and the need to develop ensuing guidance documents for regulators, operators and developers. Despite the absence of any specific guidance, and limited knowledge of methane hazards from landfill, the site was investigated and the risk assessed to the satisfaction of the developer and relevant authorities. The store consequently has a very comprehensive protection and monitoring system, even compared to later developments.

Some of the main comments made during this consultation were as follows:

1. Specialist consultants are needed to design and investigate gas risk sites and to liaise with the statutory authorities on technical issues.

2. The perceived gas risk (which is not necessarily the same as the potential gas risk) is very important, as this could affect the commercial viability of a store if the potential customers perceive that there might be a risk to the store from gas.

3. Each new site has to be treated differently because previous site investigation strategies might not be appropriate to the circumstances of the current site, although previous experience should be used where applicable.

4. It is vital that all parties concerned in the site investigation and development are made aware of the principles of the investigation and not just the procedures they should follow. To follow procedures and specifications without knowing the rationale behind them can lead to their misinterpretation or inappropriate application.

5. Timescale is a crucial factor in determining the viability of a project. It is often preferred, therefore, to opt for extra or over-specified mitigation measures in the

structure, and on the site, rather than carry out a long-term detailed investigation and assessment. Notwithstanding this, long-term reliability and monitoring of the gas-control system must be provided for.

6. Where there is scope for compromise and negotiation on the gas issues, this should be with the design and implementation of mitigation measures, not in the site investigation procedures.

7. Establishing a comprehensive and reliable dataset for such sites *via* an extensive investigation is money well spent. The developer does not want to have to change the design or layout of the proposed development as a result of something being discovered about the site, during construction, which could have been identified during an adequate site investigation.

8. An assessment of the potential gas risk and its impact upon the viability of the project should be incorporated into the initial assessment of the prospective site. Even where access is not possible (pre-acquisition), the desk study should take account of this potential. The possible cost of mitigating likely gas problems (including long-term maintenance and monitoring) should be incorporated into the initial costings of the project.

9. The likely effects on adjacent land, especially where there is existing development, should be taken into account in the design of the investigation strategy.

10. The main problems with developing gas-risk sites are that: the developer has no effective way of assessing the technical competence of the site investigation and risk assessment, or the competence of the practitioner; the statutory authorities have variable approaches and expectations of the site investigation and assessment; and, often, the authority responsible for authorising the project or assessing the gas risk assessment will not enter into consultation or negotiation prior to the work being carried out.

On the whole, active and consistent participation of the developers in the design and implementation of site investigation procedures is seen to be the best way of ensuring that the strategy employed will achieve its purpose.

4.8.2   Funders

A major funding agency was consulted for its views specifically on the investigation and development of potential gas risk sites. In general they felt that funders would need to have a very high level of comfort that the risk associated with a site (whether from methane or any other form of contamination) had been fully identified, and that the construction measures were adequate to eliminate any significant risk for an indefinite period. Reliance on management schemes, insurance cover and contingency measures against the possibility of the long-term failure of protection measures was felt to be unsatisfactory, and it was considered that this view would become more common among funding agencies. While all sites should be considered individually, development designs should err on the side of maximum protection.

4.8.3   Insurers

The insurance sector, either directly or *via* the Loss Prevention Council, made the following comments.

1. At present, methane risk to development is not considered to be a high priority issue. Rather it is a situation currently under observation and review, principally because the actual incidence of claims resulting from gas affecting property is extremely low (Loscoe being the main case).

2. Insurers generally base their premiums for domestic property on the prevalence of a particular risk in an area. For example, if subsidence claims are common in a locality, all properties in that area are likely to have a subsidence premium regardless of whether an individual property is at risk. The same protocol would be likely to apply to methane should it become a significant source of claims in an area.

3. Often properties are insured on the basis of the nature of the development and the locality, i.e. the insurers may not be supplied with or be aware of the specific details of the property, including any gas issues.

4. Insurers do not consider themselves the most appropriate party to assess the adequacy of a site investigation. Where a technical matter, such as methane risk, becomes a significant issue, most insurers would employ consultants unless they had specific in-house expertise.

5. When asked what their main requirements would be, should they specifically have to take into account the methane risk, one insurance company considered that they would need to be satisfied that the property had been constructed to an appropriate technical standard and that this had taken into account the degree of risk presented by the gas source in relation to the migration potential of the source and level of gas control on the source site.

   Interestingly, they took the sensible view that distance from the gas source site (e.g. landfill) *per se* was not a relevant consideration, as a site close to landfill in impermeable geology was probably at less risk than one further away with intervening permeable strata. In other words, there is not a direct relationship between proximity and risk.

In general, it can be taken that the insurance sector's main requirements are that the development or property should be designed with both adequate health and safety measures and risk minimisation in mind, rather than having specific requirements of the site investigation. One area of specific concern, however, is that the effect of gas on third party property is incorporated into any investigation strategy.

Allied to the insurance sector is the National House-Building Council (NHBC) who, aside from their building control function, take on a liability when issuing a warranty on new domestic properties. Unlike the insurers, however, NHBC do take a close interest in the adequacy of the site investigation where methane presents a potential risk to a new housing development.

NHBC requires builders to inform them when it is suspected that a gas source may present a risk to the proposed development and they also require the submission of all technical data, including site investigation reports, before deciding whether or not to grant warranty cover on the properties. In one case a 200+ housing development was refused NHBC cover predominantly on the basis of an inadequate methane risk assessment.

Some specific requirements of the NHBC, with respect to the adequacy of a site investigation for methane, are as follows:

1. The site investigation should assess the gas regime with respect to methane, carbon dioxide and oxygen and in relation to the water regime and barometric pressure.

2. Ideally gas flow should also be recorded.

3. Boreholes, where used, should be in accordance with the Waste Management Paper No. 27 design illustration and be of sufficient number and distribution to provide a rational understanding of the gas regime on the development site.

It would appear that the more flexible approach taken to development authorisation by the NHBC, compared to local authorities, reflects the fact that they have a national perspective on this problem and wider experience. It is worth noting that the adequacy of the site investigation and risk assessment is considered to be more important than the exclusion measures proposed, with respect to assessing the development for inclusion in the warranty scheme.

4.9 CASE STUDY EXAMPLES

4.9.1 Case study 1, freehold residential development on a former landfill site

A housing development was proposed on an infilled quarry (over 20 m deep) in an urban borough, surrounded by existing residential development. The site was filled with a mixture of wastes and known to be gassing.

Initially an application was submitted for developing the whole site with housing, which was refused because of uncertainty about the gas risk. Subsequently, following a gas investigation which provided minimal information and was of dubious competence, the developer applied for outline permission to build houses only on the parts of the site where low gas levels were measured. Again the application was refused by the planning authority on the grounds of inadequate monitoring information.

The developer appealed against the decision, arguing that sufficient information was available for outline planning permission. The appeal failed on the grounds that the site investigation was inadequate, whether for outline permission or otherwise, to assess the risk to the proposed development, which was considered to be premature for a site of this nature. A salutary lesson resulting from this was that costs were awarded against the developer because the appeal was not considered to be on reasonable grounds given the nature of the site and potential risks.

4.9.2 Case study 2, flatted development above silt deposits

A large residential block of flats was proposed on a docklands development site. The whole area had previously been the subject of a preliminary methane assessment because of the presence of silt, and the site in question had undergone a more detailed investigation (for about 1 month) prior to being sold to the developer.

The formal development proposals and construction works did not commence until approximately three years had elapsed since the gas investigations. Consequently the NHBC wanted an updated investigation, fearing that the gas regime may have changed owing to adjacent development, and there was concern that the methane generated within the silts might migrate to the surface *via* the foundation piles.

The developer subsequently commissioned a shallow probing survey of the site for construction, and no gas was found. On this basis the NHBC decided to grant the warranty, on the condition that the docklands development corporation guidelines for gas exclusion were implemented in the structure.

The developer wanted to commission a more extensive site investigation to confirm that the gas risk was low and thus negate the need for specific exclusion measures. However, the six-months to one-year monitoring that would have been expected for this by NHBC was considered too restrictive on the development programme so the developer opted for installing gas-exclusion measures instead.

4.9.3 Case study 3, housing development above abandoned coal workings

A housing development was proposed on a site in a coal mining area, adjacent to an existing housing estate. A six-month site investigation using boreholes identified a narrow zone of surface methane emission from abandoned coal workings (identified from an extensive desk study). A subsequent trial pit investigation of the whole site confirmed the thin zone of gas emission, no gas being found either side of this band.

The developer proposed a phased development and zoning of the site such that no development would take place in the area of highest emission. Adjacent to this the properties would be built with gas exclusion measures and further away the properties would be built to normal specification.

In total, monitoring and consultations lasted for two years and included spike surveys of the site to establish the shallow gas regime, in addition to the existing monitoring points. Again gas was found only in the strip (approximately 15 m wide) identified earlier.

Notwithstanding this the neighbouring residents were concerned that the gas would be forced to migrate into their estate. To allay these fears a cut-off trench was installed between the development site and the existing housing estate.

In the light of the adequacy of the investigation and the proposed development strategy the proposals were granted approval.

4.9.4 Case study 4, business development above abandoned coal workings

During consultations on a planning application for business development in a former coal mining area, the planning authority required further investigations to be carried out. Boreholes already constructed had shown the presence of mine gas at 30-40 m depth in former coal workings, but shallow probes monitored over a long period demonstrated that the overlying strata acted as an effective gas barrier. Although water has not found in the boreholes, the planning authority took the view that water levels could rise and tend to push the gas 'up-dip'. They required more detailed investigation of the 'up-dip' or western margin of the site, where they expected that the combination of gas under pressure and the thinner overlying strata would give rise to gas contamination in the shallow ground regime. Additional shallow boreholes were constructed in this area and monitored for a total of six months, but no gas was detected.

The planning permission was granted on condition that agreed gas exclusion measures were incorporated into the construction of the proposed buildings.

While no gas was detected at the western part of the site, the case illustrates the perception of risk associated with rising groundwater levels in abandoned coal mines, following the cessation of pumping (see Section 2.1.2).

5 Guidance on investigation strategies : general procedure

The discussion in the preceding Sections of the factors influencing the design of a site investigation strategy shows the way in which objectives may interact (Section 2); the characteristics of specific investigation techniques that may be employed (Section 3) and, perhaps most significantly, the extent to which these factors and techniques come into play in actual site investigations carried out by experienced practitioners (Section 4). The purpose of this and the subsequent Section is to synthesise the results of the research and current level of knowledge into guidelines for the selection of appropriate investigation strategies in the context of different gas investigation scenarios. This Section defines the procedural framework within which the specific investigation strategy should be designed.

5.1 GENERAL PRINCIPLES

It has been assumed, in the guidance given below, that the general investigation scenario is for a proposed development on a potential gas-risk site and that the end-use of the site has already been decided upon (e.g. a proposed housing estate). While there have been and will be cases of a gas assessment of a site prior to deciding the most appropriate end-use, this is rare. Where the gas investigation is required because there is a risk to existing built development the same principles apply, but the choice of technique and distribution of sampling points will primarily be determined by the access and physical constraints of the existing buildings and infrastructure.

The site investigation should be designed with the objective of demonstrating with a reasonable degree of confidence that gas does not present a risk to development. Furthermore it should be designed to provide information about the site and its environs that is not already available, and should not be seen as a method of reinforcing or duplicating existing data (e.g. geology) where those data are reliable. Development proposals frequently involve a geotechnical investigation for foundation design purposes, and wherever possible this should be adopted to include the facility for gas monitoring, where it is perceived that gas may become an important factor.

In some circumstances the gas hazard may become sufficiently well defined at an early stage of the investigation to allow development decisions to be made: this is more likely in the case of positive results. For instance, high gas concentrations detected in the preliminary investigation may lead, depending on the circumstances, either to abandonment of the project or to a decision to adopt rigorous gas control measures in the construction. Even in the latter case it may be appropriate to terminate the investigation on the basis that the design of exclusion measures does not depend on accurate prediction of gas concentrations or volumes: exclusion is as effective whether the gas concentration is 5% or 50%.

If, however, the proposed control measures incorporate venting, active or passive, the venting system must be designed with a capacity that is sufficient to maintain the gas concentration at a safe level. It is therefore necessary in this case to establish the concentration of gas and its emission rate over a representative area and timescale in order to understand the gas regime and to set design parameters; the investigation must be continued to obtain this information.

5.2 GAS INVESTIGATION SCENARIOS

In Section 2 the various factors which may have an influence upon the design of the most appropriate site investigation strategy are briefly described. While, in theory, numerous variations of strategy might seem necessary to cope with the different combinations of influencing factors, in practice the number of scenarios is greatly reduced. The conceptual models in Figures 2.2 and 2.3 reduce to the simpler form shown in Figure 5.1. This is because the only factors which ought to influence the gas

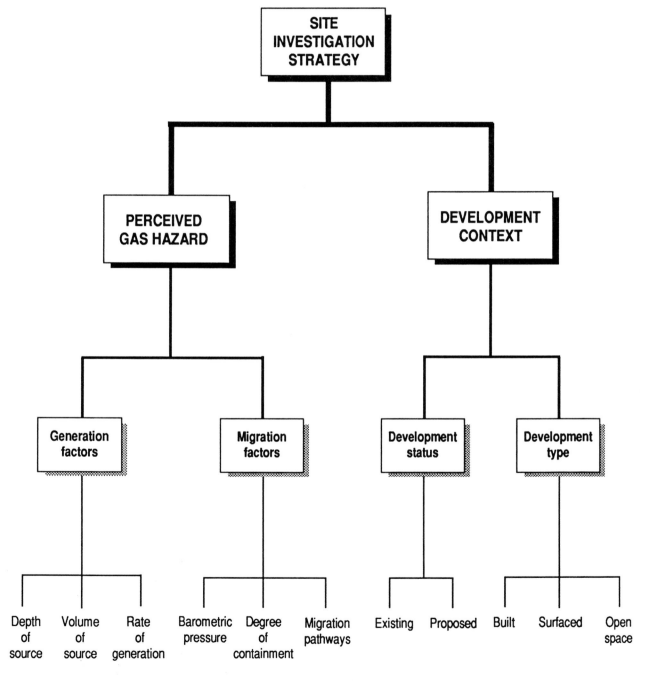

Figure 5.1 Principal factors influencing a site investigation strategy

investigation strategy are the physical factors pertaining to the way the gas hazard presents itself, and the specific circumstances of the potential receptors. The receptors or targets are basically of three types, i.e. built structures, open space and development features which enhances migration potential to other sites.

In general, the different scenarios that are likely to arise, and thus possibly require different investigation strategies, can be considered in terms of four types of development and three locations relative to the gas source.

5.2.1 Development context

Developments can be considered in four main groups (see Table 5.1). The first group relates to all kinds of buildings or surface development (residential or commercial/industrial) which may allow the accumulation of gas in voids, either within the buildings themselves or in service ducts, lighting columns, etc.

The second group comprises underground development such as tunnels and associated structures which may go through gas-bearing strata, again presenting an opportunity for gas accumulation.

The third includes development such as playing fields, golf courses, parks and landscaping, where the principal effect of gas is likely to be damage to the vegetation by root zone depletion of oxygen. However, in certain meterological conditions giving rise to an atmospheric temperature inversion, gas emitted from the ground surface may accumulate in hollows.

Table 5.1 Possible investigation scenarios

Development group	Position of development relative to gas source		
	Surface source		Subterranean source
	Within source site	Adjacent or near to source site	Above
1. Proposed buildings or surface structures	• • •	• • •	• • •
2. Proposed buried structures†	• • •	• • •	• • •
3. Open space	• •	•	• •
4. Surface-sealing development	• •	•	• •

Notes: The need for an investigation is denoted by

   • • •   investigation highly likely to be neccessary

   • •   investigation needed only in certain circumstances

   •   investigation not likely to be necessary

   †   need depends on relative depths of proposed structure and gas source

The fourth group comprises development which could inhibit or prevent gas emission through the site surface and thus promote off-site migration to adjacent land or property. Development such as car parks, roads, and surfaced playing areas would come into this category. In this group the principal risk is to third parties, rather than to the development itself.

5.2.2　Gas source

The potential gas sources can be considered as being either surface sites or as subterranean sources, i.e:

Surface gas source site	=	landfill (including sewage sludge site), peat and near surface silt or marsh deposits.
Subterranean gas source	=	mine gas, gas bearing strata and deep buried silts and peat deposits.

The position of the development relative to the gas source also affects the investigation scenario, i.e. whether the development is within or near to a surface source of gas or above a deep-seated source.

The potential for the release of methane from groundwater encountered during development may sometimes require special consideration as part of a site investigation. Significant volumes of dissolved methane are likely to be present in groundwater only where the groundwater has passed through deep gas-bearing strata and has subsequently been confined under high pressure. Usually most of the gas present is not dissolved but is part of a gas-water mixture. Nevertheless, the possibility of the movement of gas with water should always be recognised, although the presence of groundwater in itself is unlikely to indicate a need for a gas investigation.

In the specific case of landfill, gas may be generated by the degradation of the organic components of leachate even outside the boundaries of the landfill if the leachate is migrating. This will need to be taken into account in the overall site investigation strategy.

5.3　PROTOCOL FOR SITE INVESTIGATIONS

Notwithstanding that to be adequate investigations have to be site specific there is a certain degree of commonality between them. This can be used to design a general procedural framework which can then be tailored to specific situations.

Figure 5.2 is a flow chart of the broad procedural stages that should be followed in order to design a sound strategy and to execute a competent investigation. It can be considered as the core site investigation protocol for potential methane risk development sites. The variations of strategies that may be employed for different investigation scenarios all originate from this general model. The site-specific aspects of the investigation procedures are introduced at each of the various decision and action boxes. Specific selection criteria and actions required at each stage are dealt with in Section 6.

The rationale behind the flow chart is as follows:

Stage 1: A comprehensive desk study and walk-over survey should be undertaken to identify the scope and objectives of the investigation and to establish the baseline data for the site and its environs.

A decision is then taken, using this information, as to whether or not a gas investigation on the site is necessary in the near-surface ground environment or deeper.

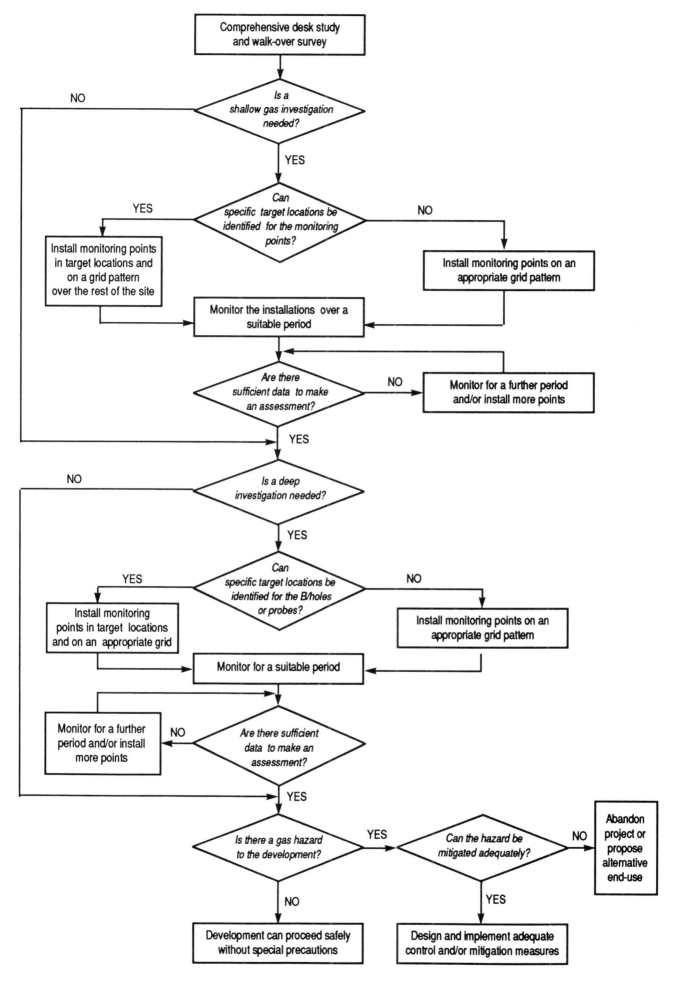

Figure 5.2 Core model for site investigation strategies

Stage 2: If it is decided that a shallow investigation is appropriate, an effective distribution and monitoring strategy should be devised using suitable techniques.

Once these installations have been monitored for a suitable period a decision has to be taken as to whether or not there are sufficient data to make a gas hazard assessment. If not, further monitoring should be undertaken involving either the existing installations and/or utilising more monitoring points or supplementary techniques until a sufficient dataset has been obtained.

Stage 3: Once the shallow gas regime has been assessed and it has been determined that there is no significant risk to the development it may be necessary to assess the gas regime at depth, e.g. where surface structures are going to have deep foundation piles.

Alternatively the desk study or project scenario might dictate that a deep investigation is needed straightaway, without an assessment of the shallow gas regime as, for example, where the proposed development is a deep tunnel.

The sequential process for the deep investigation is identical to that for the shallow investigation, although the decision criteria and influencing factors may differ.

Stage 4: Once it has been determined that an adequate dataset has been established and the gas risk defined, then the site use and/or mitigation measures can be finalised. The design of mitigation measures is not addressed here, but is the subject of a separate CIRIA report[5].

Depending upon the most appropriate route chosen through the flow chart, the general sequence of events should still follow the sequence of: desk study – preliminary investigation – detailed investigation. In some circumstances the shallow investigation would be the preliminary stage and the deep investigation the detailed one. Conversely, the detailed investigation might be the further monitoring carried out after the installation and monitoring of the shallow/deep monitoring points.

5.4   KEY ELEMENTS OF A SITE INVESTIGATION STRATEGY

The key elements and objectives of a typical site investigation strategy are as follows.

5.4.1   Desk study

The first task in every case of any gas specific site investigation, is the desk study. Moreover, where the presence of gas is suspected, no physical investigation should be undertaken until a thorough desk study has been carried out.

The main objectives of the desk study are to:
- gather as much information as possible about the site and its environs with respect to its history (e.g. types of waste, period of working), geology, hydrogeology, hydrology and topography, and about the extent and nature of existing development and infrastructure, including service locations
- identify and assess the likely magnitude and significance of the gas source or sources and indicate the potential hazard from them
- identify and evaluate the likely COSHH and health and safety implications of investigating and developing the site
- use the information gathered to design an appropriate site investigation programme, or, at least, to make a preliminary assessment.

5.4.2   Walk-over survey

A desk study is not complete unless it is also accompanied by a site visit and walk-over survey. This could be just a visual inspection of the site, but it might also include a non-intrusive surface survey of the site, services and buildings, etc. using an appropriate gas detector. There are three main objectives of a walk-over survey:

1. To relate the findings of the desk study to the site itself and its surroundings.
2. To confirm the findings of the desk study and highlight any discrepancies or anomalies.
3. To identify potential problem areas or additional significant factors not found in the desk study (e.g. new buildings, site preparation works, etc.).

5.4.3   Preliminary assessment

Whereas the desk study and walk-over survey would, on the whole, be similar for any investigation scenario, the preliminary assessment and subsequent stages will vary according to the specific investigation scenario being considered.

The main objectives of the preliminary assessment are;

- to confirm the presence of gas on the site or *indicate* its probable absence
- to give an initial indication of the gas levels that might be expected, *via* short-term monitoring
- to examine the physical nature of the ground on and around the site in question
- to identify the degree of detailed investigation required and any areas requiring special attention e.g. 'hot-spots'.

Typically the preliminary assessment will involve the use of shallow monitoring techniques such as spiking, driven probes and trial pits; that is not to say, however, that deeper techniques such as boreholes and deep driven probes are not appropriate in certain circumstances.

A preliminary assessment is characterised, usually, by the fact that the monitoring period is relatively short and the distribution of monitoring installations may be on a uniform grid pattern. The overall objective is to get an early, broad indication of the gas regime present across the site.

5.4.4   Detailed investigation

The aim of the detailed investigation is to establish a comprehensive and representative dataset of the gas regime, preferably in a worst-case situation, which will allow a confident assessment and prediction of the risk that the methane poses to the development under consideration. This is likely to be achieved where:

1. Monitoring points are installed across the site with sufficient frequency and depth to allow representative sampling of the gas body, especially in sensitive areas (e.g. zones of proposed buildings). Spacing and depths will depend on site specific factors such as the nature of the ground, the water regime and the anticipated nature of the gas source. In general, however, adequacy is likely to be determined by the total number of monitoring points and the consistency of results obtained, rather than by predetermined spacings.

2. Monitoring takes place through at least one period of rapidly falling barometric pressure and, similarly, on at least one occasion when the ground surface has been sealed by, for example, rain or frost.

3. Monitoring is carried out on a sufficient number of occasions for the results to be considered representative. i.e. a sufficient number of observations to be confident that they include an adequate variation in influencing conditions and that any trends can be recognised.

The principal influences upon the choice and employment of the appropriate monitoring strategy will be determined by:

- the findings of the desk study and preliminary investigation
- the proposed layout and design of the development
- the ground conditions of the proposed monitoring points
- the characteristics of the technique being used (e.g. how much it disturbs the ground)
- the duration of monitoring likely to be required
- the nature of the gas source.

In many cases the detailed investigation will involve the use of boreholes either as the main method of penetrating the ground mass or as a supplement to shallow probes. This is because boreholes are able to provide information on the deeper regime, where necessary; and also because the principles of their construction are well accepted and they allow the installation of robust long-term monitoring points with minimal ground disturbance.

However, boreholes may in some circumstances be unnecessary or inappropriate. In the case of very shallow fill or peat deposits, for example, shallow driven probes or probes installed in trial pits may be adequate. Where a gas source is suspected at depth (such as mine gas in old workings or landfill gas migrating along a sand or gravel layer), but it is overlain by a substantial thickness of clay or other low-permeability rock, the investigation may simply be to check for the absence of gas in the shallow regime. Such decisions can be made only in the light of all site-specific circumstances.

The typical characteristics of the detailed investigation are that it involves extensive coverage of the site, uses a variety of deep and/or shallow techniques, concentrates in sensitive locations, and monitoring occurs on a sufficient number of occasions to provide reliable data.

5.4.5   Supplementary investigation

The results of the detailed investigation could indicate areas where further investigation is required to provide either additional or supporting data.

Supplementary investigations can take the form of further coverage with techniques already employed on the site or the use of more sophisticated techniques such as analysis of lignin to cellulose ratios (to determine the gas-generating potential of wastes) or the use of flux box tests for surface emissions. The individual circumstances and findings of each investigation will determine the nature of and degree to which supplementary investigation is required.

5.4.6   Presentation of results

While the style, contents and presentation of the final investigation report are a matter of personal judgement for the author of the report, it is important for the sake of those appraising the report that sufficient information is provided to allow the reader to judge the adequacy of the investigation and the rationale for the strategy adopted. A comment made by several of the local authorities during the consultation stage was that the quality of presentation and level of detail in the report enhances greatly the degree of confidence that the authority has in the results given and the accompanying conclusions and recommendations.

The site investigation report should ideally include the following information:

- an account of the investigation procedure and the rationale for the strategy adopted and techniques used
- a detailed record of the desk study monitoring and ground investigation
- a discussion of the results relevant to the investigation objective with recommendations and supporting discussion where necessary
- a description of the control or mitigation measures to be employed (where necessary) and the rationale for the measures chosen
- any proposals for further monitoring.

5.5   HEALTH AND SAFETY MEASURES

Notwithstanding the normal health and safety procedures which should be adopted for ground investigations, the additional factors of gas and, in the case of landfill, contamination, create additional hazards which should be taken into consideration. Examples of health and safety aspects that should be considered are:

- the location of buried services
- exposure to contaminated material
- exposure to hazardous gases (explosion, asphyxiation, toxicity)
- ground instability (e.g. trial pit collapse, subsidence)
- exposure to dangerous objects (glass, syringes, metal fragments etc.).

Guidance on these and related issues is given primarily in the following publications, which also refer to other relevant documents covering specific safety matters. The implications of the COSHH Regulations (1988) should also be considered.

Health and Safety Executive, *Protection of workers and the general public during development of contaminated land*, 1991[20].

British Drilling Association, *Guidance for the safe drilling of landfills and contaminated land*, 1992[21].

CIRIA, *A guide to safe working practices for contaminated sites*, 1995[22].

6   Guidance on investigation strategies : selection criteria

The previous Section outlined the general principles of site investigation procedures and set the framework within which a specific site investigation strategy should be designed. This Section provides an explanation of the indicative selection criteria which should be used to design the most effective site investigation strategy for a given set of circumstances.

6.1   THE INVESTIGATION STRATEGY FRAMEWORK

The core strategy is illustrated in Figure 5.2. Decisions and actions are required at various stages which depend on the specific circumstances of the investigation. In order to provide guidance on the selection criteria, each stage of the framework, the core strategy, is considered separately in Sections 6.2 to 6.8 with reference to the relevant part of the flowchart. The whole flowchart is repeated for ease of reference in Figure 6.1 showing the internal cross-references.

It is essential that the limitations of these protocols are understood so that they are not misapplied. The main points are:

1. Every site is unique and the most effective investigation strategy will be one which recognises its specific environmental context and the degree of influence of the many variables affecting that site and project in particular.

2. The many variables and influencing factors make it impossible to define absolute or universal criteria. Hence professional judgement and flexibility are central to successful implementation of site investigation procedures and to the appraisal of the results.

3. In order to illustrate how typical strategies are developed, various scenarios are used as examples. While based on realistic situations, they have been simplified to highlight particular aspects. The guidance they give is therefore indicative, not definitive, and should not be taken as a prescription.

4. Official guidance must also be considered where professional judgement considers that it is appropriate and providing that reasoned interpretation is applied rather than dogmatic compliance.

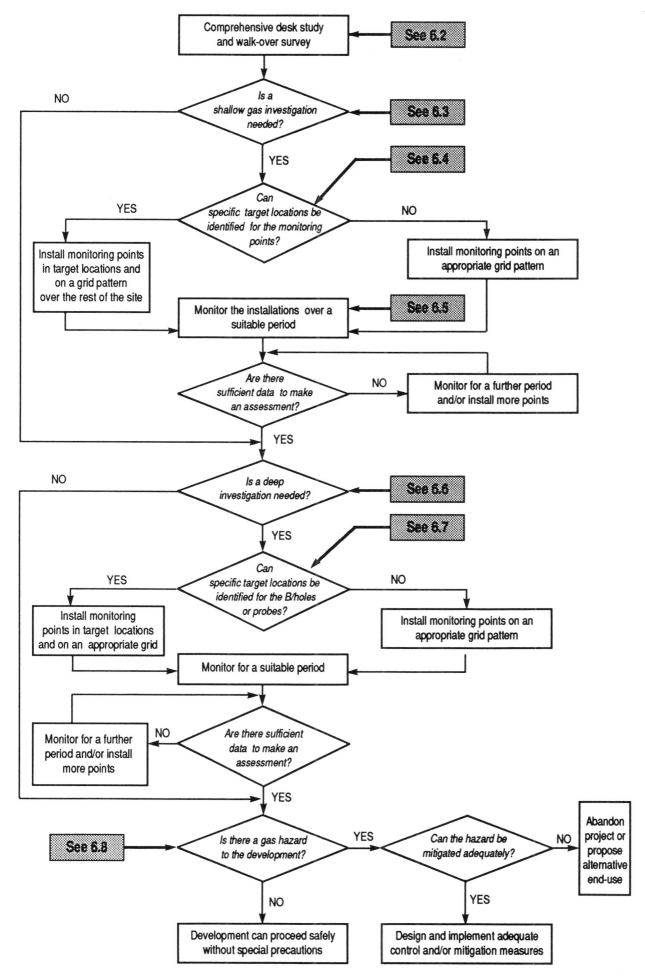

Figure 6.1 Annotated core model for site investigation strategies

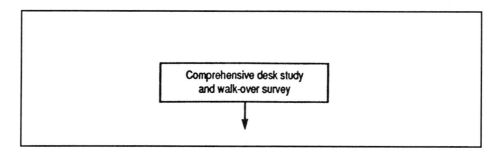

6.2.1   **Desk study**

Every site investigation for methane should begin with a comprehensive desk study. This should incorporate all available information about the site and its surroundings. The desk study should address three main aspects of the site and its proposed development.

1. *Physical context* : the physical context of the site, its surroundings and the gas source (where this is not on the development site) should be defined. This should include the layout of the site, topography, geology, hydrogeology and hydrology.

2. *Site history* : an attempt should be made to identify the nature and location of former uses of the site and its surroundings, especially where the potential gas risk is from a former landfill. In this case information should be obtained on the size, depth, waste types, age and operation of the site, particularly with regard to its environmental controls.

   Where the potential gas risk is from abandoned mine workings the desk study should attempt to establish the extent and location of the workings, whether gas and groundwater control measures were employed, and if so when their use ceased.

   The desk study should also attempt to identify any former uses of the site and its surroundings which could provide gas migration pathways, e.g. old access roads, service runs or demolished buildings.

3. *Current use* : the use to which the site and surroundings are currently put should be identified and compared with the historical information. This may for example indicate the presence of infilled areas not identified on any records.

   The assessment of current use should include the identification of such features as buried services and infrastructure, which could provide migration pathways.

   In cases where the potential gas risk is from an operational landfill or active mine workings, attempts should be made to assess the degree of gas control currently being exercised at these facilities. This could give an indication of the magnitude of the gas risk and, in the case of active mine workings, it is important to confirm with the mineral manager that the proposed investigation will not compromise gas control measures by 'short circuiting' the ventilation system.

The principal points of good practice with respect to the desk study are:

- gaining as much information as possible from whatever sources are available. The relevance of the available information should be assessed after it has been obtained and examined in detail, rather than prejudged, otherwise potentially useful data might be missed

- inspecting all records in person, wherever possible, thus allowing professional informed judgement of which data are relevant, rather than delegating this to the holder of the information

- confirming all significant information in writing where appropriate
- regarding anecdotal evidence with caution. While potentially useful it must be regarded as indicative at best unless corroborated by other reliable data
- even where the principal gas source is obvious, always attempting to identify other potential gas sources
- being prepared to expand or direct the desk study as necessary during the subsequent site investigation where the circumstances dictate this to be appropriate.

The principal sources of information for a desk study are shown in Table 6.1. Although the list is not exhaustive it should be noted that much of the information needed may not officially be within the public domain, and the provision of such information is often discretionary. A more detailed account of potentially useful sources is given in Reference 8.

6.2.2   Walk-over survey

A site visit and walk-over survey should always accompany a desk study, since it is important that the findings of the desk study are put into the perspective of the actual site and its surroundings. More specifically, the site visit and walk-over survey should, wherever possible:

- confirm the site boundary and location/orientation and dimensions of visible surface features and structures in relation to the site plans, OS maps and aerial photographs
- locate and identify surface features and structures not indicated on site plans/maps/photographs etc.
- locate and identify services and service access points
- identify areas of stressed vegetation and/or dieback, subsidence/settlement, ponded or unusual surface water (colour, odour, etc.), strong vapour haze or steam from discrete areas, etc.
- identify strong or unusual odours, gas bubbles in ponded water or wet ground, areas of elevated temperature (e.g. thawed ground or melted snow)
- identify the physical state and nature of capping/cover material on any adjacent/nearby landfill (e.g. vegetated or waste visible, etc.).

In addition to the visual inspection of the site, additional information can be gathered using specialist techniques ranging from a 'sniffing' exercise with a flame ionisation gas detector to sophisticated techniques such as infra-red aerial surveillance or thermography (see Reference 3).

Table 6.1 Sources and nature of information which may be used for a desk study

Statutory authority sources*	Nature of the information/data
Waste Regulation Authority Waste Disposal Authority	Landfill site licences, site operational history environmental controls and local waste arisings.
Environmental Health Authority	Closed landfill (pre-1974) and industrial site records, current pollution problems.
County/District Planning Authority	Proposed/existing development plans and records, aerial photographs, local maps and plans, geological data, development history.
Building Control Authority	Site records and design for previous, existing and proposed buildings on or adjacent to the site.
Local Library/Archivist	Historical data on developments and incidents on the site and the surrounding area.
National Rivers Authority	Hydrological, hydrogeological, geological and pollution incident data.
Health and Safety Executive	Geological, mining and technical data for the area or type of site in question.
Other organisations/records	
British Geological Survey	Geological maps and records.
Ordnance Survey	Topographical data, location of potential receptors, indications of former use.
British Coal	Mining records and abandonment plans.
Utilities Companies	Location and nature of services (especially underground supply and town gas).
Local Water Companies	Similar data to NRA plus potential methane in groundwater occurrence, sludge disposal records.
Industrial Registers	Former and existing use of industrial sites or areas.
Developers and Consultants	Existing site investigation reports and data for previous development proposals on or adjacent to the site.
Anecdotal sources	
Local Residents	Unrecorded tipping or mining activity, historic incidents and *approximate* dates and locations of activity.
Former/Existing Employees	Specific details of the site or previous incidents or problems.

* Note the future Environment Agency will represent a consolidation of these sources of information.

6.3 NEED FOR A SHALLOW GAS INVESTIGATION

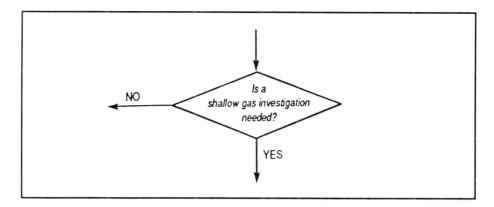

A shallow gas investigation (of the order of 5-m depth or less) is likely to be needed where surface development exists or is proposed on a potential gas-risk site and where the potential gas hazard arises from any of the following (see Figure 6.2):

- a landfill site
- shallow mine workings
- shallow gas-bearing strata (e.g. coal measures)
- peat or silt deposits
- deep gas-bearing strata or mine workings where the desk study indicates that there may be a migration pathway to the surface zone, such as fissures or shafts
- deep gas sources where no migration path is suspected but confirmation of this is required from investigation of the shallow zone.

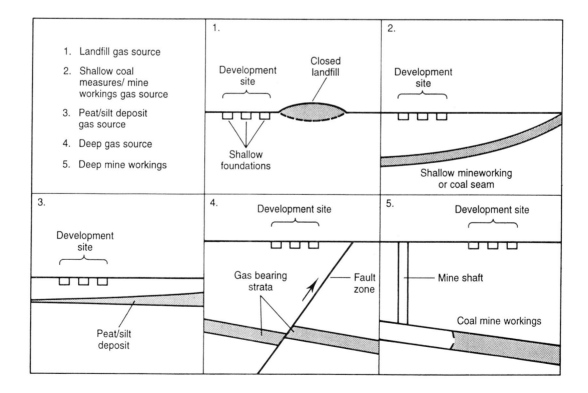

Figure 6.2 Examples of shallow gas investigation scenarios

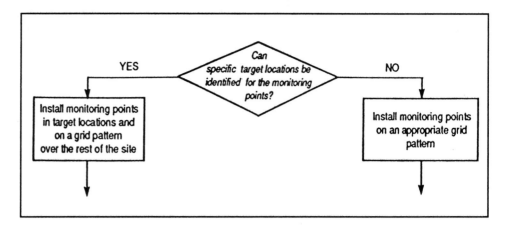

6.4.1   Identifying specific target locations

Specific target locations for monitoring installations should be those areas of the site which will be more sensitive to the gas risk or which enhance the risk by their physical nature (e.g. by providing accumulation points in void space under buildings or migration pathways). Typical examples of these are the proposed locations of (see Figure 6.3):

- building plots
- service ducts and man-holes
- foundation footings
- lighting columns, electrical control cabinets and similar structures
- deep-rooted planting (e.g. shrubs and trees)
- roads, parking areas and similar surface sealing features.

In all cases, specific target locations for monitoring should be those areas of the site where the desk study has indicated that the likelihood of finding gas is higher. On a landfill site for example these might be areas of:

- deeper waste deposition
- die-back or elevated temperature
- putrescible waste deposition.

On a development site adjacent to a landfill these areas could be:

- the site perimeter nearest the landfill site
- close to roads or other potential surface migration conduits which pass from or near the landfill to within or close to the development site
- close to zones of permeable geology which may intercept the waste mass in the adjacent landfill.

Where the principal gas source is coal measures or similar gas-bearing strata, key target locations would be where workings, veins or permeable geology which are contiguous with the gas body pass under or outcrop near to the development site.

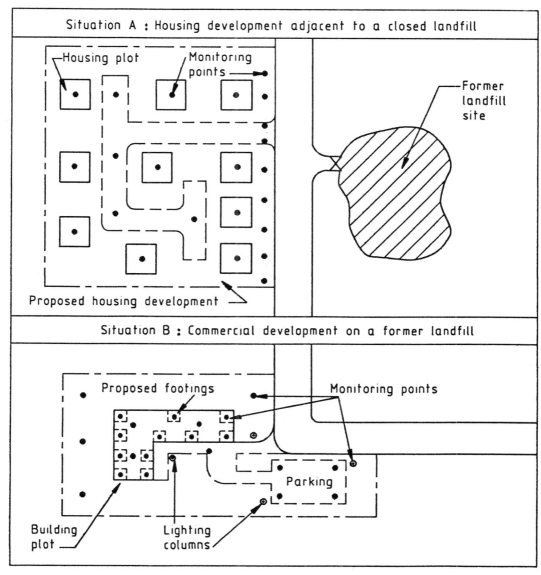

Figure 6.3 Examples of spacing strategies

6.4.2   Selection of appropriate grid patterns

Where there may be insufficient information to identify target locations for the monitoring points either on the whole site or parts of the site, the method most likely to give a representative indication of the gas regime is to install the monitoring points on a uniform grid pattern. The spacing between points should vary according to the specific context of each site.

In general the spacing criteria used in WMP 27 can be taken as the starting point and tailored to the specific requirements of each site.

The spacing chosen initially should reflect the perceived magnitude of the gas risk to the development as, for example, in the following ways:

1. Where the gas hazard is perceived to be high, i.e. there is a high probability that gas will be present on the site, a wide spacing of monitoring points *might* be adequate to confirm this and to enable appropriate measures to be taken.

2. Where the gas hazard is perceived to be high, but is not confirmed by a widely spaced grid, the spacing density should be increased either to confirm the presence of gas or to have confidence that it is absent, i.e. a more extensive search is required to be sure of the absence of gas.

3. Where the gas hazard is perceived to be low, i.e. there is a low probability that gas will be found on the site, again a wide grid spacing *might* suffice to confirm this perception. If gas is found, however, further installations could be needed to allow a full assessment.

4. Where the likely magnitude of the gas hazard is unknown, it should be assumed to be high (i.e. worst-case scenario) and thus points 1 and 2 apply.

The actual spacing chosen for each of the above scenarios should be site specific. In general the onus of proving a negative, (i.e. that the original perception of gas hazard was wrong), will necessitate more work than confirming the original perception was correct.

Typical indicative information for establishing whether the magnitude of the gas hazard should be perceived as high or low is shown in Table 6.2.

Strategies have been developed for the representative spatial sampling of contaminated land on the basis of statistical analysis[23]. However, this approach relates to the determination of the minimum number and locations of sampling points necessary to identify 'hot spots' of various dimensions, assuming that there is no significant mobility of contaminants. This is difficult to apply to a gas investigation, given the mobility of the gas body and its potential to expand or migrate over relatively large areas. A 'representative' spacing of sampling points is more likely in this case to be related to the minimum total number of points needed to give confidence in the spread of results.

For example, four monitoring points giving consistent results of 1% LEL *might* be taken to be representative, especially on a relatively small site and where the results were replicated from one monitoring occasion to another. If, however, results ranged from 1 to 50% LEL, there could be no confidence from such a small number of points that in other parts of the site, or on other occasions, concentrations would not exceed the LEL, even in the case of a relatively small site. Conversely, a results range of 1 to 50% LEL *might* again be taken as representative if it was obtained from a hundred points, almost regardless of the size of the site.

It is important to note that these figures are intended not to constitute specific guidance, but to illustrate the difficulty of adopting predetermined sampling point spacings. The conclusions to be drawn are that:

*   the monitoring pattern should be decided on the basis of judgement and experience, taking account of all the specific circumstances of the site; and

*   the monitoring pattern may have to be altered or extended in the light of the results obtained.

Table 6.2 Indicative information of gas hazard

Source	Low perceived gas hazard	High perceived gas hazard
Landfill site	Small sites which have taken inert wastes, wastes with a low putrescible fraction (e.g. construction wastes and certain industrial wastes) and old domestic landfills (pre 1950 accepted mainly ash and glass)	Small and large recent/current domestic waste sites or sites taking industrial/commercial wastes with a high putrescible content (e.g. food wastes)
Peat deposit	Low volume deposit, dewatered, unvegetated or worked deposit	Extensive vegetated deposit, with high anaerobic/waterlogged portion
Silt deposit	Low volume dewatered or dry deposit with little or no cover	Extensive waterlogged, covered deposit
Mine gas	Currently active or recently finished workings with gas and water control measures in operation, deep workings surrounded by impermeable strata, submerged workings	Abandoned workings with no active control measures, or rebounding water table, extensive shallow workings
Gas-bearing strata	Deep or less extensive measures overlain by low permeability strata or below groundwater level	Extensive measures, near the surface or at depth, but in contact with permeable strata

6.5   MONITORING REGIME

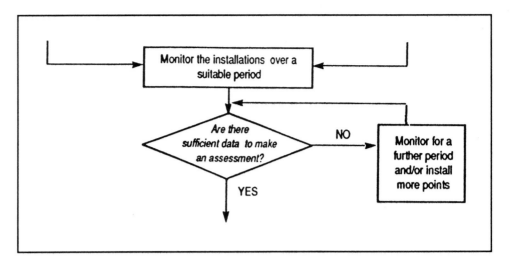

The monitoring regime comprises the parameters to be monitored and the duration and frequency of monitoring required to provide an adequate dataset such that a confident assessment can be made.

6.5.1   Monitoring parameters

The concentration of each of the components of the gas mixture should be measured, and specifically for:

- methane
- carbon dioxide
- oxygen.

The limitations of field equipment must be acknowledged in recording the results (see Reference 3). For example, where the field instrument indicates volume concentrations of $1\%^v/_v$ methane or less, the reading should be confirmed with a more sensitive device (0–100% LEL or 0–10 000 ppm sensitivity) or samples taken for laboratory analysis, since some field instruments cannot resolve below 2% methane and may thus indicate significant gas where there is in fact none.

Likewise, where oxygen is depleted (i.e. below approximately $15\%^v/_v$) LEL-methane values should be disregarded (where these are obtained using a catalytic oxidation device) and only percentage gas in air should be recorded.

The gas emission rate is as important as gas concentration for assessing the gas regime, although it is much more difficult to measure, particularly where emission rates are low. This is typically the situation of interest, however, as gas investigations are frequently used to demonstrate the absence of a gas problem. Where the emission rate is high then the gas risk is obvious and the need for further investigation may be reduced, unless quantitative data are required for the design of extraction measures.

In addition to the direct gas measurements, the weather conditions and their effect on the ground conditions prior to monitoring should be observed and recorded, in particular the amount of precipitation and its effect on sealing the surface of the gas source site (especially a landfill) and the rate of change of barometric pressure, especially if falling.

Since the other main influencing factor upon the gas regime and its effective migration is groundwater, i.e. it can act either as a barrier to significant gas movement or as a transport medium for the gas, groundwater conditions should be monitored wherever possible. Consequently it is preferable during a shallow investigation to have some piezometers or standpipes, which can be dipped and sampled, either adjacent to or within the monitoring installations. This is particularly important where leachate migration from a landfill site is suspected. It is possible, of course, that no water may be encountered in the shallow regime or it may only be temporary or perched water; nonetheless its presence should be sought and monitored where found.

On each monitoring occasion, the gas concentrations should be recorded initially on opening up the monitoring installation and should continue until either a steady reading is obtained or the borehole is evacuated (i.e. ambient readings are obtained). In addition the highest methane and carbon dioxide readings should be noted.

All relevant information such as water level, ground conditions, barometric pressure, etc. should be recorded. Table 6.3 lists the information that should be recorded and the purpose of recording it.

It is preferable that all this information is recorded on each and every monitoring visit, although in some circumstances this may not be possible or appropriate. It is important, however, that the ambient conditions are recorded whenever possible because they influence the interpretation of the gas concentrations and emission rates.

Moreover, where data from two separate investigations of the same site are being assessed, information on ambient conditions may allow reasons for differing results to be identified, e.g. lower gas concentrations associated with higher water levels from the later investigation could indicate the sealing of migration pathways by rising groundwater.

In addition, this information will allow anyone undertaking a technical appraisal of the results to judge whether or not the data were obtained competently (e.g. correct choice of equipment).

An example of a monitoring record form is shown in Appendix B.

6.5.2   Monitoring duration and frequency

The initial monitoring might comprise a one-off spike survey or an intense period of trial pit or driven probe observations to get an early indication of the gas regime. In general, however, monitoring should take place on 6 to 10 separate occasions before any confident decisions can be made. The key criteria to satisfy (which may necessitate exceeding the above guidance) are:

- monitoring occasions should cover a range of weather conditions and atmospheric pressure and include at least one period of falling barometric pressure and one of heavy precipitation (preferably combined)

- the gas regime should be progressively monitored as the above conditions develop and if such conditions occur between scheduled monitoring visits an extra monitoring visit should be attempted if possible

- where stable atmospheric and ground conditions occur over a period of time regular monitoring should be undertaken to establish if there are any fluctuations in the gas regime independent of the above influencing factors

- where the water regime fluctuates (e.g. tidal water) gas monitoring should take place through and after the fluctuation cycle to determine if this influences the gas regime either immediately or with a time lag.

The principal aim of the monitoring should be to measure the gas regime during the worst-case conditions in relation to influencing factors. It is also necessary to confirm that this is the worst case by monitoring when those conditions are not present. These worst case conditions are site specific.

The conditions which normally have the greatest influence on gas migration are rapidly falling barometric pressure and/or surface sealing by water. However, this may not always be the case. For example, prolonged periods of high barometric pressure and low rainfall may cause depression of the water table, which might have been preventing gas accessing permeable strata; consequently gas migration could be enhanced under such conditions (see Figure 6.4). Clay strata may also become more permeable to gas in prolonged dry spells.

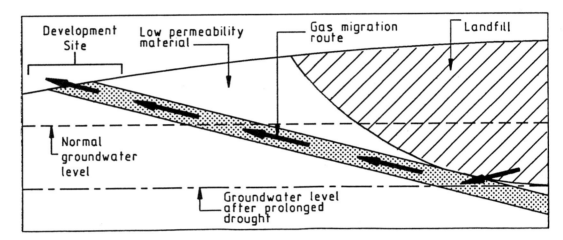

Figure 6.4 Example of gas migration promotion by depression of the water table

The recovery period that should be left between monitoring visits is highly site specific, and must be a matter for experiment. If frequent monitoring takes place, and the probe is evacuated of gas and this does not have time to build up again before the next monitoring visit, then this in itself could indicate that the gas generation or migration rate at that point is low. However, it is still necessary to be confident that a maximum concentration has been obtained in order to assess the possible long-term accumulation of gas in a potential structure. If rapid-frequency monitoring does not evacuate the monitoring point and consistently high readings are obtained this indicates that the gas generation or migration rate is high.

Where the monitoring strategy has shown results throughout the monitoring period which indicate that gas is not present or is present below levels which could be considered hazardous, and this is confirmed, then it is reasonable to conclude that the gas hazard is negligible. Where gas levels are consistently high it may be possible to conclude early in the monitoring programme that mitigation measures are necessary. Where there is uncertainty, however, and gas levels fluctuate around a critical value (e.g. 1% methane), or there is no clear trend, further investigation should be carried out.

This further investigation should include any one or more of the following

- installing additional monitoring points to give a greater density of coverage
- using additional techniques such as lignin/cellulose ratio analysis, flux box tests, etc.
- further regular monitoring of the existing installations for a longer period
- a combination of any or all of the above.

The main objective of the further investigation should be to provide sufficient supplementary data to allow a confident assertion that the gas risk from the shallow regime either is or is not significant.

Table 6.3 Typical information to be recorded on each monitoring occasion

Information	Significance
A. *Influencing conditions*	
1. Change in barometric pressure up to 24 hours prior to monitoring and before and after sampling.	A rapid rate of rise or fall in barometric pressure could influence the results
2. Ground conditions e.g. dry or desiccated, waterlogged, snow covered, frozen, etc.	The degree of surface sealing may affect the results
3. Weather conditions e.g. raining, windy, hot, etc. prior to and at the time of monitoring	Apart from the effect on ground conditions weather can have effects such as diluting surface emissions in strong wind, prolonged heavy rain could surcharge the water table, etc.
4. Groundwater level	Groundwater can act as a piston on the gas body above it, or cut off or open up migration routes to the monitoring points
B. *Gas monitoring results*	
1. Initial concentration of CH_4, CO_2 and O_2	For 1-5 the factors observed are all indicative of the gas body into which the monitoring point has been installed, i.e. the results can indicate whether the gas in the installation is just a static accumulation (e.g. rapid fall off from initial reading) or a constantly replenished emission
2. Steady state concentration of CH_4, CO_2 and O_2	
3. Highest concentration of CH_4 and CO_2 (where not already encountered)	
4. Indication of rate of fall/rise of concentration from the initial reading (i.e. rapid or slow).	
5. Emission rate of the gas	Indicates the potential for migration and potential rate of accumulation in a confined space
6. Composition and concentration of any duplicate gas sample taken for laboratory analysis	Should be recorded at the time of sampling to allow confirmation that the sample is representative or that the field instrument is calibrated correctly
7. Record of procedure followed	
C. *Monitoring equipment*	
1. Type and make of field instrument used and its last calibration date	This confirms that an appropriate piece of equipment has been used and that it is verified as calibrated
2. Type of gas monitoring installation	Confirms the adequacy of the installation for the regime being assessed.
3. Physical condition of the monitoring point (e.g. opened, vandalised, blocked)	Indicates whether the monitoring point is still effective
4. Depth of monitoring/sampling	

6.6 NEED FOR A DEEP GAS INVESTIGATION

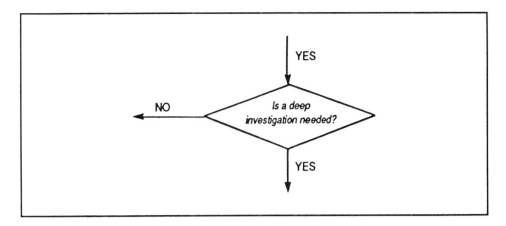

A deep gas investigation is likely to be necessary under the following circumstances:

1. Where the gas source is at depth (e.g. coal measures or mine gas) or where the gas-generating body is deep, e.g. landfill.

2. Where the proposed development involves piled foundations, or part of a structure itself, into potential gas-bearing strata at depth.

3. Where permeable or potential gas-transmitting strata are contiguous with a gas source and extend below the development site (e.g. mineworkings, or sand lenses which intercept waste).

4. Where the proposed development involves the construction of deep buried structures (e.g. tunnels) which pass through gas-bearing strata.

5. Where the intervening geology and hydrogeology between a suspected deep gas source and the development site is not known.

The building of surface structures in an area where there are suspected gas-bearing strata at depth does not in itself necessitate a deep investigation. Provided deep foundations or services are not proposed, a shallow investigation may suffice to demonstrate that the shallow ground regime (i.e. the interface between the ground and the proposed structure) is unaffected by gas. This is particularly so when the gas-bearing strata are known to be overlain by a substantial thickness of clay or low-permeability rock.

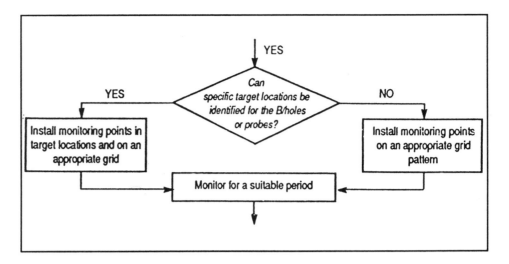

The criteria for deciding upon the distribution of deep monitoring installations are, in principle, the same as those for shallow installations, and likewise for the monitoring strategy. There is, however, an additional criterion, namely the depth to which the installation should be constructed.

The depth of installation should be determined by the nature of the gas source as follows:

1. Where the gas source is mine gas or gas-bearing strata, the borehole should extend to the depth of the gas source and preferably be of a multi-probe type so that the gas regime at successive depths in the intervening geology can be monitored.

2. Where the gas source is an adjacent landfill the monitoring points should extend to below the maximum depth of the wastes or the groundwater level, whichever is lesser. On this latter point care must be taken to establish if the water encountered is the groundwater table or perched or fluctuating water. Furthermore, although groundwater typically inhibits gas migration it can act as a transport medium for gas or as a gas source itself where contaminated with high-strength leachate.

3. Where permeable rocks such as sandstones or fracture zones come into contact with a gas source such as mineworkings or a waste mass, the monitoring points should penetrate to the depth of such strata where they pass near to the development site. Intervening strata should also be monitored at varying depths to identify any lateral migration.

4. Where the proposed development is a tunnel, the boreholes should be sunk to below the proposed depth of the tunnel and should be placed along the line of the tunnel.

5. Where the development site is on a deep former landfill, the monitoring points should not penetrate the base of the site and if possible their number should be minimised, since the ingress of air or water *via* the borehole may activate or inhibit gas generation or otherwise alter the gas regime.

Notwithstanding the observations made in Section 6.6, gas detected at depth indicates a potential gas risk to the development if future activity or changes in ground conditions provide a migration pathway to the surface. The likelihood of such pathways being created may have to be considered in assessing the need for a deep gas investigation.

Monitoring of the hydrogeological regime, while not unimportant at shallow levels, becomes especially significant for deeper investigations, and should include consideration of the possible carriage of dissolved gas particularly within confined aquifers.

An additional factor which should be taken into account with deep monitoring installations is the volume of gas that needs to be sampled to ensure that the equivalent volume of the borehole or sampling tubes has passed through the instrument.

It is important that when borehole monitoring installations have served their purpose and are no longer required, their locations are accurately recorded and that they are sealed to prevent gas migrating up the borehole into any structure that may be built above them in the future.

6.8   ASSESSING THE INVESTIGATION RESULTS

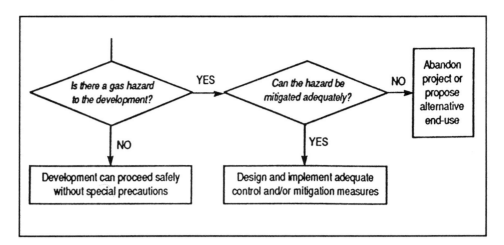

The analysis of the results of a gas investigation, the resulting assessment of hazard and risk and their implications for the nature and construction of the proposed development, are being considered in current CIRIA projects. Consequently, only a very general indication of the assessment stage of the procedure is given here.

If the investigation confirms that gas concentrations and emission rates are so low that they do not present a hazard to the development, and are unlikely to in the future, works may proceed without incorporating any specific gas exclusion or control measures. The levels below which no explicit hazard may be considered to exist are indicated, in respect of landfill gas, by the criteria quoted in Waste Management Paper No. 27 for the cessation of gas monitoring, namely: 1% $^V/_v$ methane and 1.5% $^V/_v$ carbon dioxide, over a minimum period of at least two years and as measured on at least four occasions. Since monitoring may cease below these levels, they may be considered to represent the limits below which unprotected development may take place, provided there is no reason to expect future changes in the gas regime. For other gases, the hazard implications can be assessed by reference to the occupational exposure limit set by the Health and Safety Executive[6].

Where gas levels in excess of these are found, the risk to the specific development is assessed by taking into account not only the gas regime but also the nature of the development, the methods of construction and the context of related hazards. For example:

- the gas regime identified may be considered to pose a significant risk to a housing or office development comprising predominantly small rooms with minimal levels of ventilation, but not to a warehouse or hangar with an open side or large doors

- a structure to be built on a solid floor slab with no service penetrations is likely to be at less risk than the same structure on strip footings with a suspended floor, given a similar gas regime

- an industrial building which is intended to have internal atmospheric monitoring and high ventilation levels because, for instance, of the possibility of process vapours or dusts, could be at no additional risk from the presence of gas in the underlying ground.

The assessment of risk will lead to decisions on the acceptability of the development and the nature of any gas control measures. Proposals for private housing, for example, may be altered to corporately managed housing to prevent the erection of casual structures (sheds, greenhouses) with insufficient protection against gas ingress; or to another use altogether such as light industry. In extreme cases the idea of built development might be abandoned.

There is a wide range of possible gas exclusion and control measures available to suit the development and the level of risk[5]. They range from single barrier exclusion methods, such as a solid floor slab in a building, to multi-barrier exclusion systems (floor slab plus membranes and /or sealants at appropriate positions) with active gas ventilation measures and continuous atmospheric monitoring. In some cases ground engineering systems, such as the installation of an impermeable cut-off at the boundary of the development, would be more appropriate. The selection of control measures is always site specific and is again a matter for experience and judgement.

It should be noted that where venting of gas forms part of a proposed control system, it is usually necessary for the gas investigation to have provided sufficient information on the volumetric aspects of the gas regime to allow the ventilation measures to be designed effectively.

While long-term monitoring may be necessary in some cases – especially where a gas hazard has been detected after development has taken place – gas control measures ought, in general, to be sufficiently rigorous and robust to give complete confidence in their long-term performance without the need for monitoring. Post-development monitoring can involve logistical, commercial and legal complications which are best avoided.

7　Further study

As with all research projects and reviews, areas of deficiency in current understanding and scope for improvement in practice can be identified. In relation to the hazards of methane and associated gases to development, and their investigation, the particular areas for further study are discussed briefly below.

7.1　OVERVIEW

This report has described current practice in the investigation of sites for methane and associated gases and has given guidance for undertaking such investigations. This guidance, however, has relied strongly upon the use of indicative rather than absolute criteria. Although this is primarily a function of the site specificity of gas risk it is also a consequence of the many uncertainties in understanding both the gas regime and the adequacy of the investigation techniques.

In the light of this, further study into the gas regime and the way it behaves in relation to its environs, including artificial disturbance by monitoring installations, could identify trends and properties which could allow more definitive and standardised guidance to be produced in the future. It may be possible, for example, to quantify migration potential in relation to the specific geological setting of the gas source and its generation characteristics. Notwithstanding the value of such quantitative criteria, however, the issue of site specificity will always take precedence in the design of any site investigation.

Broadly, the two main areas where further study might prove useful are:

1. Developing understanding of how gas behaves and interacts with its environment to give rise to a gas risk, and designing or refining methods to quantify and predict this.

2. Developing understanding of how gas can be controlled or excluded and defining the limitations of control systems with respect to the gas hazard.

At present the predominant source of methane which is of concern is landfill. Mine gas is perceived to be less of a problem nationally. This balance, however, may change. Almost all recently opened and certainly all future landfill sites will have gas control systems and are likely to be operated on a containment basis. Consequently, uncontrolled gas emission and migration leading to explosion and other risks, will become more and more improbable and are only likely to occur in the event of significant failure of the control system. If reasoned judgement is applied, then in future, i.e. once the activity of current gassing and uncontained sites has expired, landfill gas should be treated in a similar manner to town gas, i.e. its presence should be accepted and understood by virtue of its being confined in a controlled engineered system. Special investigations and extensive mitigation measures in proposed properties should not be necessary. Furthermore, it would be illogical, for example, for a waste regulation authority to issue a completion certificate to a site, indicating that the site will no longer give rise to pollution, and a planning authority to require a gas investigation for development adjacent to the same site.

Mine gas, however, may become more of a problem as mining activity and the related control measures decline, given that there are likely to be perhaps several million cubic metres of methane present in some of the more extensive workings.

7.2   SPECIFIC RECOMMENDATIONS

The gas hazard for any target is determined by the amount of gas which presents the hazard and its ability to migrate to the target. This in turn is a function of available migration pathways and factors which influence gas movement such as gas pressure, rate of generation, etc. At present these relationships are largely defined qualitatively.

Empirical guidelines could be derived from studies of the effect of the rate of barometric change and differential pressure change on gas migration, such as:

- critical rate of change of barometric pressure to promote or inhibit gas movement (e.g. +/- X mb/hr)
- dilution factors through permeable strata of known permeability (e.g. what distance/depth of material is safe to dilute the gas to negligible levels?)
- relationship between emission rate and migration potential
- volumes and pressures of gas which can be tolerated by specific control or exclusion systems.

While this list is not exhaustive it highlights some of the areas where defined criteria could be of substantial value in the near future and would, for example, allow more informed and accurate prediction of zones of influence or risk around landfill sites, rather than the arbitrary 250-m rule applied at present. For example, it should be possible to undertake some kind of qualitative evaluation of all the gas monitoring results held by investigations and assess these in the context of the specific physical, geological, and environmental context of each site investigated. This might help to identify underlying trends or relationships.

References

1. HARTLESS, R. (Compiler)
    Methane and associated hazards to construction : a bibliography
    Special Publication 79, CIRIA, London, 1992

2. HOOKER, P.J. and BANNON, M.P.
    Methane and associated hazards to construction
    Report 130, CIRIA, London, 1993

3   CROWHURST, D. and MANCHESTER, S.J.
    The measurement of methane and other gases from the ground
    Report 131, CIRIA, London, 1993

4   STAFF, M.J. and SCEAL, J.
    Methane and associated hazards to construction: research and information needs
    Project Report 5, CIRIA, London, 1993

5   CARD, G.B.
    Protecting development from methane
    Report 149, CIRIA, London, 1995

6   HEALTH AND SAFETY EXECUTIVE
    Guidance Note EH40 : Occupational exposure limits
    HSE, 1992

7   BARRY, D.L.
    Hazards in land recycling: In: *Recycling derelict land*
    (G. Fleming ed.), Thomas Telford, 1991
    pp. 29-63

8   BRITISH STANDARDS INSTITUTION
    BS 5930: 1981 Code of practice for site investigations
    BSI, London

9   BRITISH STANDARDS INSTITUTION
    Draft for Development - *DD175: 1988 Code of practice for the identification of contaminated land and its investigation*
    BSI, London

10 DEPARTMENT OF THE ENVIRONMENT
    Waste Management Paper No. 27 (2nd edition), Landfill gas
    DoE, 1991

11 DEPARTMENT OF THE ENVIRONMENT
    Waste Management Paper No 26, Landfilling wastes
    HMSO, London, 1986

12   DEPARTMENT OF THE ENVIRONMENT
     Circular 21/87, *Development of contaminated land*
     HMSO, London, 1987

13   CROWHURST, D
     Measurement of gas emissions from contaminated land
     Report BR100, BRE, 1987

14   DEPARTMENT OF THE ENVIRONMENT
     Circular 17/89, *Landfill sites : development control*
     HMSO, London, 1989

15   INTERDEPARTMENTAL
     COMMITTEE ON THE REDEVELOPMENT OF
     CONTAMINATED LAND (ICRCL)
     Guidance note ICRCL 17/78, Notes on the development and after-use of landfill sites
     DoE, 1990

16   BUILDING RESEARCH ESTABLISHMENT
     Construction of new buildings on gas contaminated land
     BRE, Garston, Watford 1991

17   DEPARTMENT OF THE ENVIRONMENT
     Building Regulations 1991 Approved document C, Site preparation and resistance to moisture
     HMSO, London, 1992

18   INSTITUTE OF WASTES MANAGEMENT
     Monitoring of landfill gas
     IWM, 1989

19   LEACH, B.A. and GOODGER, H.K.
     Building on derelict land
     Special Publication 78, CIRIA, London, 1991

20   HEALTH AND SAFETY EXECUTIVE
     Protection of workers and the general public during development of contaminated land
     HSE, 1991

21   BRITISH DRILLING ASSOCIATION
     Guidance notes for the safe drilling of landfills and contaminated land
     British Drilling Association, Brentwood, Essex, 1992

22   STEEDS, J.E., SHEPHERD, E. and BARRY, D.L.
     A guide to safe working practices for contaminated sites
     Report 132, CIRIA, London (in press)

23   FERGUSON, C
     The statistical basis for spatial sampling of contaminated land
     Ground Engineering, Vol. 25, No. 5, 34-38 June 1992

Appendix A   Organisations consulted

CONSULTANTS

Clayton Environmental Consultants
Frank Graham Consulting Engineers Ltd
Charles Haswell and Partners Ltd
Industrial Research Services
Wardell Armstrong
Wimpey Environmental Ltd

LOCAL AUTHORITIES

Dudley Metropolitan Borough Council - Environmental Health Department
Greater Manchester Waste Regulation Authority
Kent Waste Regulation Authority
London Borough of Bexley - Planning and Building Control Departments
London Borough of Hounslow - Planning Department
London Waste Regulation Authority
North Warwickshire District Council
Sheffield City Council - Geotechnical Services Department
West Lothian District Council
West Yorkshire Waste Regulation Authority

DEVELOPERS

Barratts (Midlands) Ltd
Countryside Properties Ltd
National Westminster Bank Plc
North West Water Plc
J Sainsbury Plc

INSURERS AND FUNDERS

Loss Prevention Council
National House-Building Council
National Westminster Bank Plc
Sun Alliance International

PROFESSIONAL INSTITUTIONS

Institution of Environmental Health Officers
Royal Town Planning Institute

Appendix B   Gas monitoring record form

Site: Date: Time: Operator:

Weather conditions:	
Surface ground conditions:	
Barometric pressure trend (24 hr):	
Barometric pressure: Start of sampling visit	End of sampling visit
Monitoring equipment:	Date of last calibration:

Gas monitoring results:

Ambient concentration (% Volume): CH$_4$ CO$_2$
O$_2$

Monitoring Point		Gas concentration							Gas emission rate	Comments
		Initial		Highest		Steady				
No.	GWL	CH$_4$	CO$_2$	CH$_4$	CO$_2$	CH$_4$	CO$_2$	O$_2$		
	(m)	Note 3	(%)	Note 3	(%)	Note 3	(%)	(%)	Note 4	
1										
2										
3										
4										
5										

Notes

1. Comments box should include reference to the condition of the monitoring installation (e.g. blocked, open) or any other relevant information.

2. Groundwater level (GWL) should be recorded in the monitoring point wherever possible or within the site generally (from dedicated standpipes) if necessary.

   Establishing the water level within the monitoring installation is important as it confirms that the monitoring point was effective (i.e. the water level was not so high to prevent gas entering the monitoring point) in addition to allowing an assessment of the relationship between gas concentration/emission and water level.

3. The methane concentration units should be entered in the box with the numerical value, according to the instrument or scale used, i.e. ppm, LEL, % gas

4. Gas emission rates should be entered in the appropriate box with the numerical value according to the instrument used, e.g. m/s, l/min.

UNIVERSITY OF STRATHCLYDE

30125 00517769 5

#35306551

S/0:ML
NO INF.

CIRIA Report 150

1995

Methane investigation strategies

J G Raybould, S F Barry, L Barry

D
624
RAY

ANDERSONIAN LIBRARY
★
WITHDRAWN
FROM
LIBRARY
STOCK
★
UNIVERSITY OF STRATHCLYDE

CONSTRUCTION INDUSTRY RESEARCH AND INFORMATION ASSOCIATION
6 Storey's Gate, Westminster, London SW1P 3AU
E-mail switchboard @ ciria.org.uk
Tel 0171-222 8891   Fax 0171-222 1708

UNIVERSITY OF
STRATHCLYDE LIBRARIES

Summary

This report gives guidance for good practice in the design and execution of site investigations for methane and associated gases in the ground. The report was prepared following a comprehensive review of current guidance documents and detailed consultation with practitioners, developers, local authorities, funders and insurers. The guidance given is intended to be indicative rather than prescriptive, and the importance of site specificity is emphasised. The report gives an account of the literature review and consultations, and describes good practice for site investigations with the aid of tables, a flowchart and examples. Emphasis is given to the procedures and strategies which should be adopted rather than specific techniques, although a brief account of these is also given.

J G Raybould, S P Rowan and D L Barry
Methane investigation strategies
Construction Industry Research and Information Association
Report 150, 1995

ISBN 0 86017 435 2

ISSN 0305 408 X

© CIRIA 1995

Keywords		
Methane, Landfill gas, Carbon dioxide, Site investigation		
Reader interest	**Classification**	
Construction and environment professionals, Developers, Planners	AVAILABILITY	Restricted
	CONTENT	Guidance based on best current practice
	STATUS	Committee guided
	USER	Construction professionals, developers and statutory authorities

Published by CIRIA, 6 Storey's Gate, Westminster, London SW1P 3AU. All rights reserved. No part of this publication may be reproduced or transmitted in any form or by any means, including photocopying and recording, without the written permission of the copyright holder, application for which should be addressed to the publisher. Such written permission must also be obtained before any part of this publication is stored in a retrieval system of any nature.

UNIVERSITY OF STRATHCLYDE
28 MAR 1996
UNIVERSITY LIBRARY

This report was issued as Core Programe Funders Report 14, in November 1993, to Core Programme sponsors/project funders. Since its initial issue it has been subject to minor corrections.